DANT
INFER

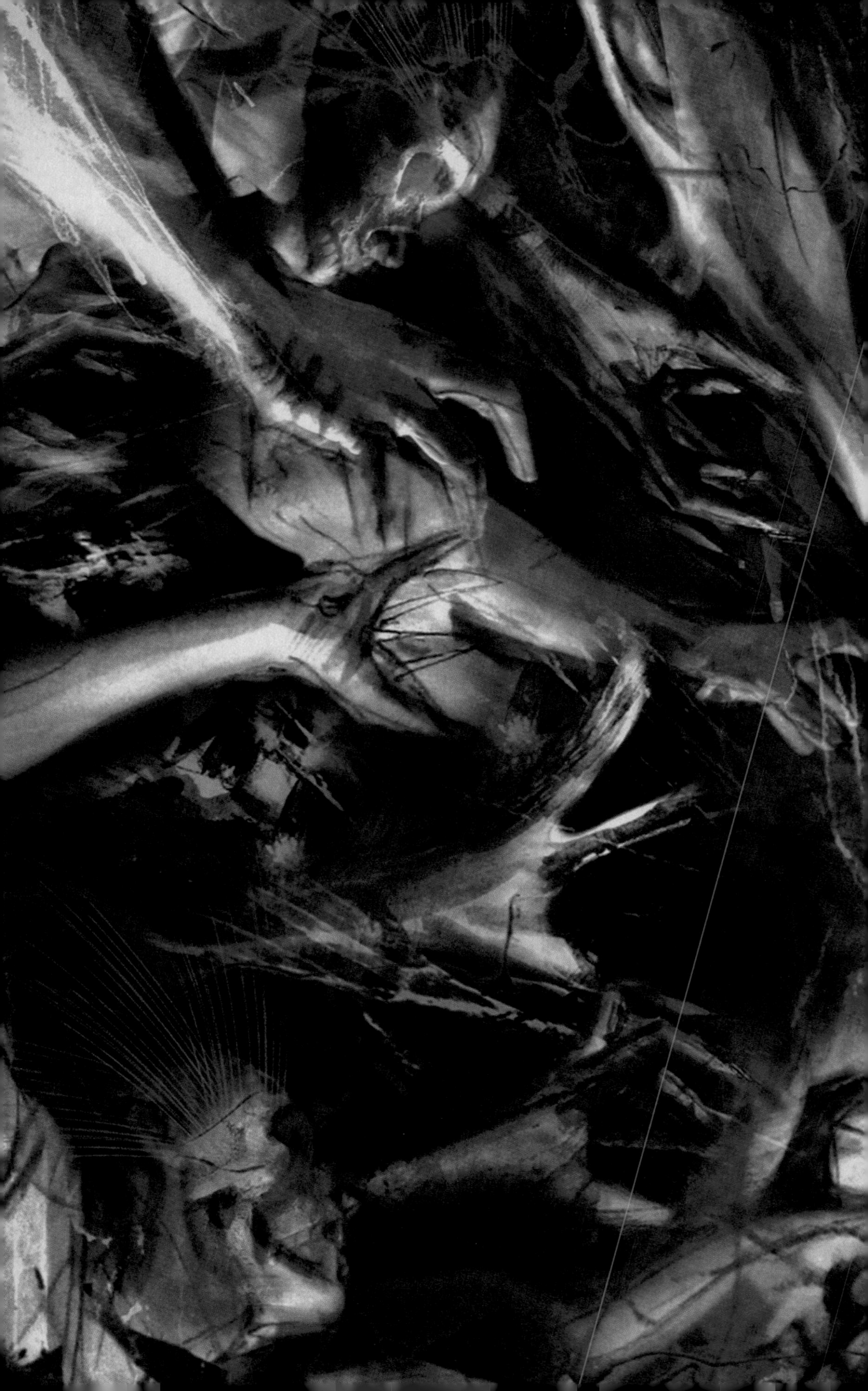

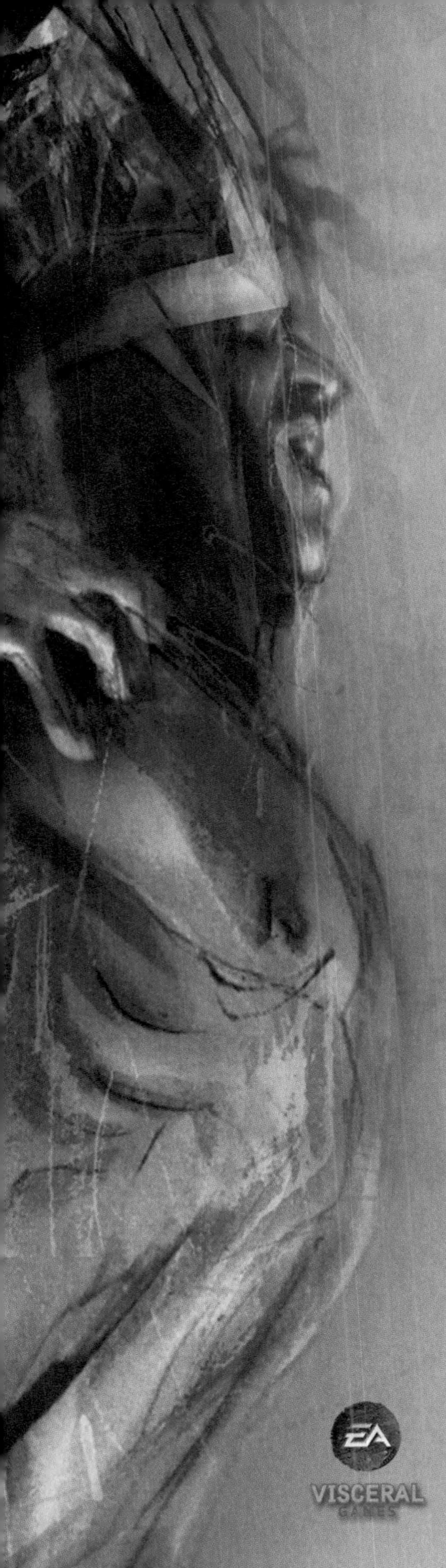

CHRISTOS GAGE
writer

DIEGO LATORRE
artist

ROB LEIGH
letterer

Scott Peterson	Editor
Kristy Quinn	Assistant Editor
Ed Roeder	Art Director

Diane Nelson	President
Dan DiDio and Jim Lee	Co-Publishers
Geoff Johns	Chief Creative Officer
John Rood	Executive Vice President–Sales, Marketing and Business Development
Patrick Caldon	Executive Vice President–Finance and Administration
Amy Genkins	Senior VP–Business and Legal Affairs
Steve Rotterdam	Senior VP–Sales and Marketing
John Cunningham	VP–Marketing
Terri Cunningham	VP–Managing Editor
Alison Gill	VP–Manufacturing
David Hyde	VP–Publicity
Hank Kanalz	VP–General Manager, WildStorm
Sue Pohja	VP–Book Trade Sales
Alysse Soll	VP–Advertising and Custom Publishing
Bob Wayne	VP–Sales
Mark Chiarello	Art Director

Special thanks to Jonathan Knight, Justin Lambros, Cate Latchford and the DANTE'S INFERNO team at Visceral Games.

DANTE'S INFERNO, published by WildStorm Productions. 888 Prospect St. #240, La Jolla, CA 92037. Compilation, game art cover and sketches Copyright 2010 © Electronic Arts Inc. All Rights Reserved. Originally published in single magazine form as DANTE'S INFERNO #1-6 © 2010 Electronic Arts Inc. All Rights Reserved.

DC Comics, a Warner Bros. Entertainment Company.

ISBN: 978-1-4012-2812-5

Chapter One
Damnation

Florence, Italy.
The Middle Ages.
MY NAME IS BEATRICE.
MY MOTHER TOLD ME THAT IT MEANS "SHE WHO BLESSES." BUT WHEN I STUDIED THE CLASSICS, I BECAME AWARE OF ANOTHER DERIVATION.
"BEATRICE" LIKELY COMES FROM "VIATRIX"--LATIN FOR "VOYAGER."

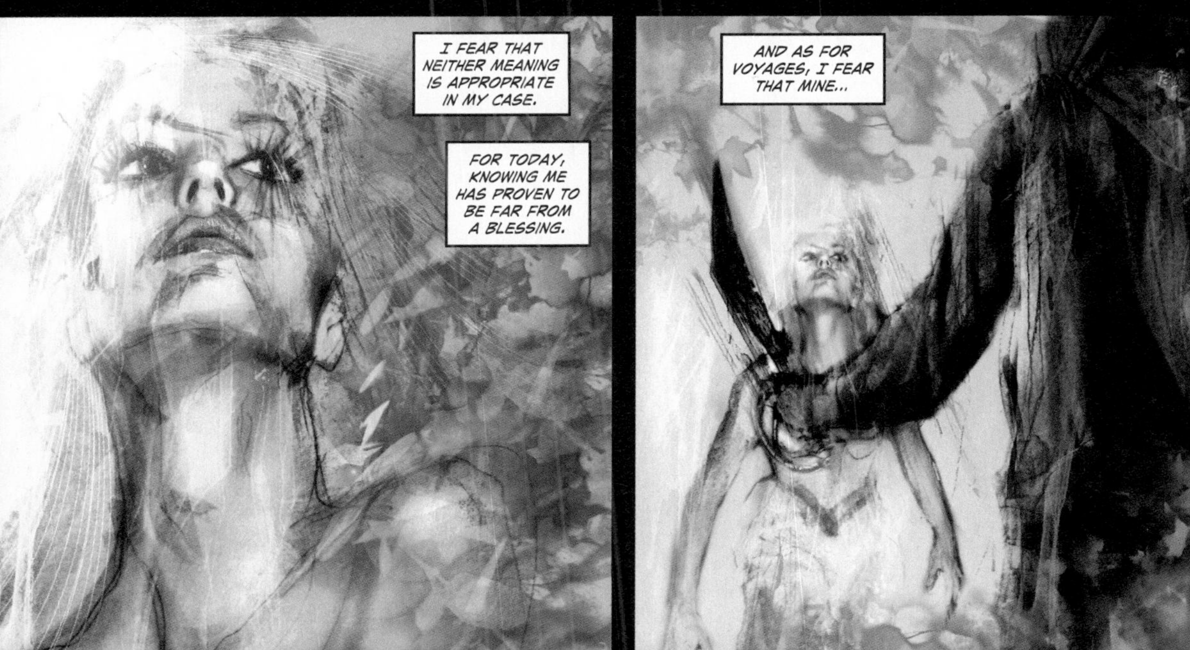
I FEAR THAT NEITHER MEANING IS APPROPRIATE IN MY CASE.
FOR TODAY, KNOWING ME HAS PROVEN TO BE FAR FROM A BLESSING.
AND AS FOR VOYAGES, I FEAR THAT MINE...

...IS AT
AN END.

SOLDIERS SAY THE ONE WHOSE NAME IS ON YOUR LIPS WHEN DEATH COMES MUST BE YOUR TRUE LOVE.
DANTE...
I DID NOT NEED TO DIE TO KNOW MINE.

DANTE...
I HAVE KNOWN FROM THE MOMENT WE FIRST MET.

HAD I DOUBTED, EVEN A BIT, I WOULD NEVER HAVE GIVEN MYSELF TO HIM OUTSIDE THE HOLY BONDS OF MARRIAGE.
BUT I DID SO WILLINGLY. EAGERLY. KNOWING WE WOULD BE TOGETHER FOR ALL TIME.

WHEN THE CRUSADE IS OVER, WE SHALL BE WED. I PLEDGE THIS TO YOU. I PLEDGE MYSELF TO YOU.
AND I TO YOU, DANTE. ALWAYS.

DANTE...I KNOW GOD WILL BE WITH YOU, FOR IT'S HIS WORK YOU DO. SO PERHAPS IT IS A SIN FOR ME TO FEEL THIS WAY...BUT I FEAR FOR YOU.
THERE'S NO NEED. WE GO TO LIBERATE THE HOLY LAND FROM HEATHEN HANDS. THE BISHOP HAS SWORN TO US THAT WE SHALL BE PROTECTED.
EVEN SO...TAKE MY CROSS. CARRY PART OF ME WITH YOU... A SAFEGUARD FOR YOUR SOUL, AS YOUR ARMOR SHIELDS YOUR BODY. A SYMBOL OF MY LOVE AND FIDELITY.
AND I SURRENDER TO YOU MY HEART, WITH A PROMISE TO FORSAKE ALL OTHERS, ALL PLEASURES OF THE FLESH. MY ONLY THOUGHT IS OF THE MOMENT WE CAN BE TOGETHER AGAIN.
KEEP YOUR SPIRIT LIGHT, BEATRICE. PLAN OUR WEDDING. AND LOOK, AS I DO, TO THE DAY OF MY RETURN.
I DID AS HE BADE ME. THOUGH HIS ABSENCE WAS A DULL, EVER-PRESENT ACHE, I FIXED MY GAZE ON THE FUTURE.
I SWEAR BY GOD IT WILL BE THE FINEST FEAST FLORENCE HAS SEEN. EVERY MAN SHALL AVER THAT ALIGHEIRO SPARED ***NO EXPENSE*** ON HIS SON'S MARRIAGE...A CELEBRATION FIT FOR A KING!
AND IN THIS GOWN, YOU'LL PUT ALL THE QUEENS OF EUROPE TO SHAME, *eh*, BEATRICE?
AS YOU SAY, MOTHER. FOR MY PART, I WOULD GLADLY WEAR SCULLERY RAGS IF IT MEANT MY BELOVED HAD RETURNED.
I WANTED SO MUCH TO BELIEVE MY LOVE'S WORDS. THAT WE WERE PROTECTED. THAT THE HORRORS OF WAR COULD NOT TOUCH US.
I WAS WRONG.

FOR A MOMENT I DARED HOPE IT WAS HIM.
YOU! WHAT BUSINESS HAVE YOU HERE?
SPEAK, PEASANT, OR--
--YOU DARE?!?
AND THEN ALL HOPES WERE DASHED.
NONE OF US KNEW HIM. BY HIS DRESS, HE WAS FROM FOREIGN LANDS. YET HE SLEW MY FATHER AND MOTHER WITH THE SAVAGERY, THE HATE...
RUN, BEATRICE!
RUN!
EEAAA--
...OF ONE AVENGING THE MOST GRIEVOUS WRONG.
TO THE LAST, I BELIEVED WITH ALL MY HEART THAT DANTE WOULD COME FOR ME.
SAVE ME.

HE DID NOT.
BUT ANOTHER DID.
SO BEAUTIFUL...

LADY BEATRICE.
MY CONDOLENCES ON YOUR UNTIMELY PASSING.

AWAY, EVIL ONE. I KNOW WHAT YOU ARE.
YOU HAVE NO CLAIM ON ME, LUCIFER.
IT'S TRUE. YOUR SOUL IS BEYOND MY REACH.
YOUR HEART, HOWEVER IS QUITE ANOTHER MATTER. BEHOLD.
"DANTE..."
"OBSERVE THE MAN YOU LOVE ON HIS NOBLE CRUSADE. TELL ME, IS IT ALL YOU IMAGINED?
"SEE HOW HE SLAUGHTERS NOT JUST SOLDIERS, BUT CIVILIANS...WOMEN, BOYS AS YOUNG AS TEN, ATTACKING HIM WITH PRIMITIVE WEAPONS THAT POSE NO TRUE THREAT.
"AND YET HE SPILLS THEIR BLOOD WITHOUT HESITATION. DARE I SAY IT, WITH RELISH.
"ASK YOURSELF, FAIR BEATRICE... WHERE MUST THE SOUL OF A MAN WHO COMMITS SUCH DEEDS SPEND ETERNITY?"

TRICKS. DECEPTIONS FROM THE PRINCE OF LIES.
IT...DOES NOT MATTER. HIS CAUSE IS HOLY.
THE VISION I HAVE SHOWN YOU IS TRUE. YOU KNOW THIS.
WAIT... THAT IS THE MAN WHO SLEW ME. WHAT...
...NO. NO!! DANTE!
...BEATRICE...
SHINK SHINK
DANTE, YOUR FATE IS DECIDED. COME, FACE ETERNITY. AND SOON YOU SHALL BE JOINED BY THOSE WHOSE LIVES YOU HAVE RUINED, WHOSE SOULS YOU HAVE DAMNED.
YOUR LADY LOVE FOREMOST AMONG THEM.
BEATRICE...?
NO.

NO!!
SPECTER OF DEATH, I DEFY YOU!

I DENY YOU!

DEATH CANNOT STOP ME. HELL ITSELF CANNOT IMPEDE MY COURSE.
IF ANY EVIL DARES CAST ITS SHADOW OVER MY BELOVED...
...IT SHALL KNOW MY WRATH!
IF YOU TRULY BELIEVE THAT, I SHALL MAKE A WAGER WITH YOU.
IF DANTE HAS BEEN TRUE TO YOU, I SHALL RELINQUISH ANY CLAIM ON HIS SOUL...NOW AND FOREVERMORE.
BUT IF HE HAS NOT... YOU SHALL BE MINE.
YOU SEE! HE COMES! HE HAS SLAIN DEATH TO RETURN TO MY SIDE!
THIS IS PROOF...PROOF THAT HIS HEART IS TRUE!
POOR, LOYAL BEATRICE.
WELL? WHY DO YOU HESITATE, WHEN A MOMENT AGO YOU WERE SO CONFIDENT?
MY...MY MISTRUST IS NOT OF HIM, BUT YOU. HOW CAN I BELIEVE ANYTHING YOU SAY?
EVEN THE DEVIL HIMSELF MUST KEEP HIS WORD. AND I PLEDGE TO YOU THAT I SHALL SHOW YOU NO FALSE VISIONS OF DANTE.
LISTEN TO HIM, PROCLAIMING HIS HONOR. I AM NO FOOL. LUCIFER MAKES NO BARGAIN THAT DOES NOT BENEFIT HIM.
AND YET... IF DANTE'S SOUL IS TRULY AT RISK OF DAMNATION... I MAY BE HIS ONLY HOPE.

I ACCEPT.
SUCH DEVOTION. SUCH FAITH. IT IS THIS THAT PLACED YOU BEYOND MY REACH...
SEE HOW YOUR BELOVED ACTED WHEN HE WAS FAR FROM YOUR LOVING ARMS.
OBSERVE THE TRUE MEASURE OF YOUR DANTE'S CHARACTER.
DANTE? BUT...WHO IS...
OH, GOD, NO...
...OH, DANTE...
I AM HERE.
BEATRICE...?
NO! BEATRICE!
I TOLD HIM YOU WOULD COME FOR ME.

BUT I MUST GO WITH HIM, MY LOVE. I GAVE MY WORD.
WITH--?
STOP!
WHAT FOUL SHADOW IS THIS, THAT TAKES MY BELOVED FROM ME?
YOU KNOW ME WELL, FOOL.
CONJURO TE, SPIRITUM HUMANUM!
BRRRAM
FORGIVE MY RUDE DEPARTURE, DANTE. I DO HAVE MUCH TO THANK YOU FOR. IT WAS YOU WHO DELIVERED THE SOUL OF YOUR LOVE INTO MY HANDS.
SADLY, I MUST AWAY. BUT ALLOW ME TO LEAVE YOU WITH A PARTING GIFT.
THE EMBRACE OF THE UNQUIET DEAD.

NO!!!
BEATRICE! I WILL SAVE YOU!
YES, YES. WE'VE HEARD YOUR EMPTY PROMISES BEFORE.
AND WE SEE WHERE THEY'VE BROUGHT US.
HAHAHA
HAHAHA!

THIS PLACE... IS IT--
MERELY AN UNCONSECRATED CATHEDRAL.
KRAKAKOOOOM
BUT FEAR NOT, MY LADY. I SHALL OPEN THE WAY...
...AND YOU WILL SOON REACH YOUR NEW HOME.

BEATRICE!!
WHY, DANTE?
WHY DID YOU BREAK YOUR PROMISSSE...

WHAT HAVE I DONE?
THE SPECTRE OF DEATH SPOKE TRULY. MY BELOVED SUFFERS FOR MY SINS.
I SHOULD HAVE LET HIM TAKE ME. I SHOULD LET THESE UNDEAD HORRORS TAKE ME NOW. DAMNATION IS NO LESS THAN I DESERVE.
...DANTE...
BEATRICE...?
DANTE, DON'T GIVE UP. IF YOU LOVE ME, YOU WON'T GIVE UP...
DAMN ME FOR A WEAKLING. FORGIVE MY WORDS, LORD. AND GIVE ME STRENGTH...

...THAT I MAY REDEEM MYSELF!
HE IS PERSISTENT. UNRELENTING IN PURSUIT OF HIS GOAL. HE VERY WELL MAY REACH IT.
AND WHY NOT? GIVEN HIS DEEDS IN LIFE, AT SOME POINT, IT WAS INEVITABLE THAT HE PASS THROUGH--
--THE GATES OF HELL.
GOD HELP ME...THERE? HE TAKES ME IN THERE?

I...I CANNOT...I AM SORRY, MY LOVE. I CANNOT MANAGE THIS ALONE AND KEEP MY SANITY. I...
WAIT.
I RECOGNIZE YOU, SHADE. MANY TIMES HAVE I SEEN YOUR LIKENESS IN MY STUDIES, RENDERED ON SCULPTURES OF THE ANCIENT WORLD.
YOU ARE VIRGIL, ARE YOU NOT? MOST EXALTED OF THE POETS?
YOU... KNOW ME? AFTER ALL THESE MANY YEARS?
I DO. PLEASE...YOU MUST AID ME. I FEAR MY FRIEND HAS GONE ASTRAY.
HELP HIM, VIRGIL, THAT HE MAY COME TO ME. I AM BEATRICE. AND WHEN I AM FINALLY BEFORE THE LORD--AS I HAVE FAITH I MUST BE--I WILL PRAISE YOU TO HIM.
HAVE COURAGE, BEATRICE. I SHALL DO ALL THAT I MAY, WITHIN THE BOUNDS OF MY CURRENT SORRY STATE.
SPEAK NOT TO THE SHADES, MY DEAR. THEY ARE SMALL, FILTHY THINGS.
YOU HAVE A FAR GREATER DESTINY IN STORE.
PLEASE, VIRGIL. I BEG YOU...
FAITH, FAIR BEATRICE. FOR TODAY I HAVE LEARNED THAT EVEN IN HELL...
...A SOUL MAY FIND REDEMPTION.

I HAVE NEVER BEEN HERE BEFORE, AND YET I KNOW WHAT I LOOK UPON. I HAVE SEEN IT IN MY DARKEST MOMENTS.
GUARDIAN OF THE GATES OF HELL, HAVE PITY ON ME, WHATEVER YOU ARE. I AM DANTE, AND I MUST PASS THIS WAY.
BEG NOT MY PITY, FOR ONE FAR MORE WORTHY HAS GIVEN YOU HERS.
I AM VIRGIL, THE POET. AND I WILL AID YOU TO THE EXTENT I AM ABLE.
POET, GIVE ME STRENGTH. I WILL DELIVER MY LOVE FROM THIS FATE, WHATEVER THE COST.
THAT, I AM AFRAID I CANNOT DO. IN HELL, THERE IS BUT ONE WAY TO FIND STRENGTH, AND I AM FORBIDDEN TO REVEAL IT.
BUT I SHALL TRAVEL WITH YOU, AS YOUR GUIDE, IMPARTING WHAT KNOWLEDGE I AM PERMITTED.
YOU WILL FIND ME AGAIN ON THE OTHER SIDE. BUT FIRST, DANTE, YOU MUST ENTER. AND YOU HAVE MADE A GRAVE MISJUDGMENT.
FOR I AM NOT THE GUARDIAN OF THE GATES OF HELL.

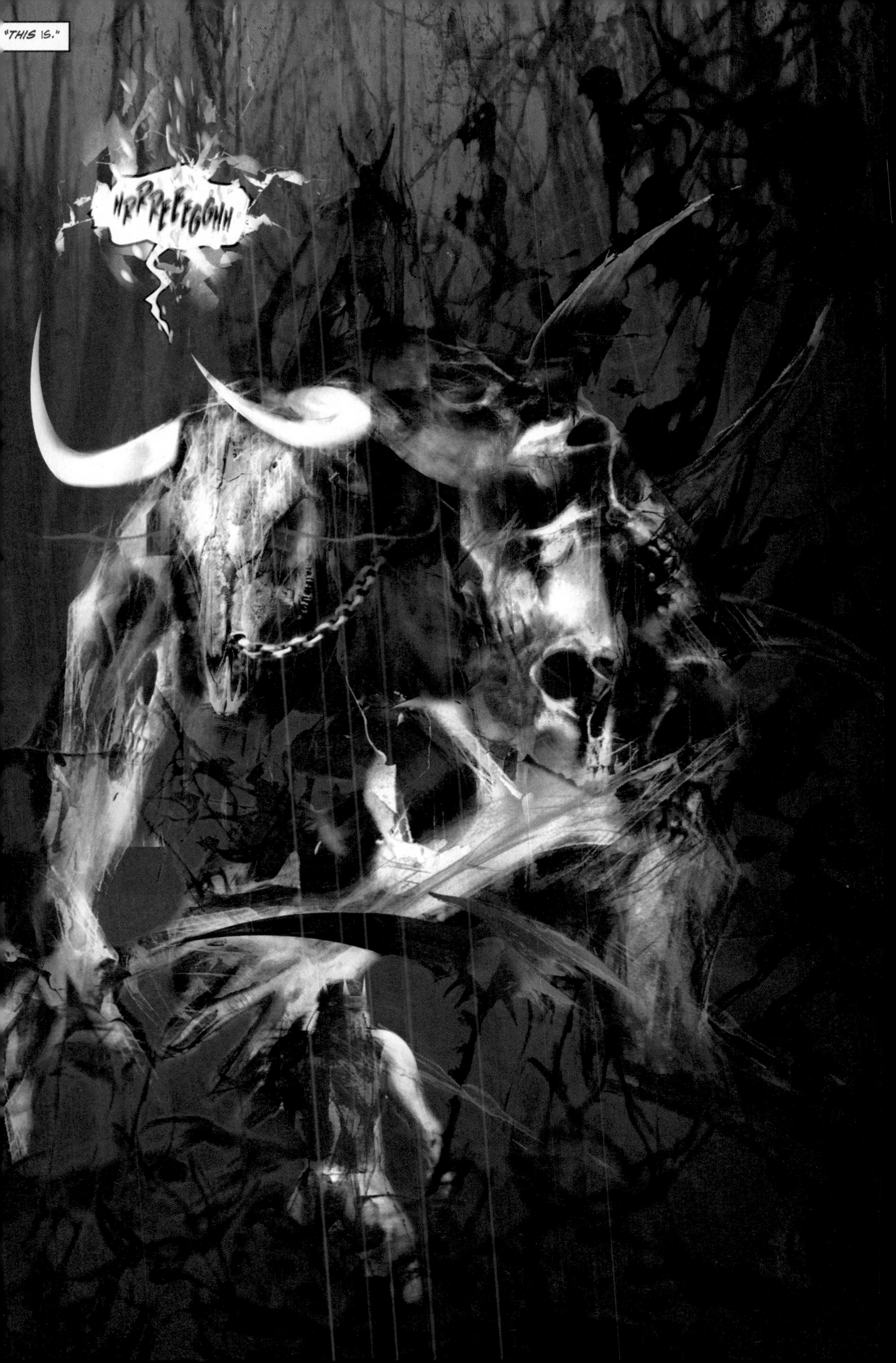
"THIS IS."
HRRREEEOGHH

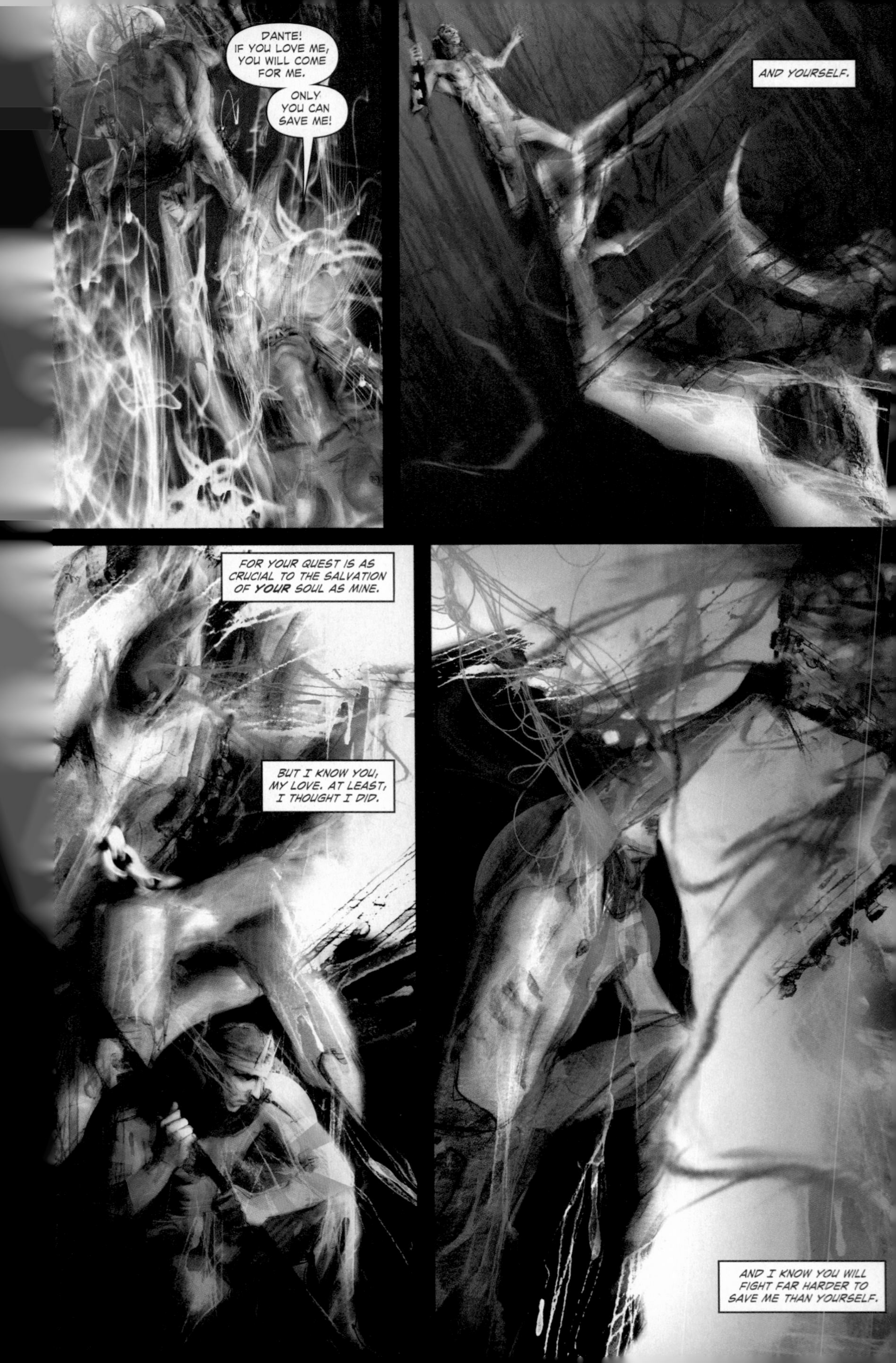
DANTE!
IF YOU LOVE ME, YOU WILL COME FOR ME.
ONLY YOU CAN SAVE ME!
AND YOURSELF.
FOR YOUR QUEST IS AS CRUCIAL TO THE SALVATION OF YOUR SOUL AS MINE.
BUT I KNOW YOU, MY LOVE. AT LEAST, I THOUGHT I DID.
AND I KNOW YOU WILL FIGHT FAR HARDER TO SAVE ME THAN YOURSELF.

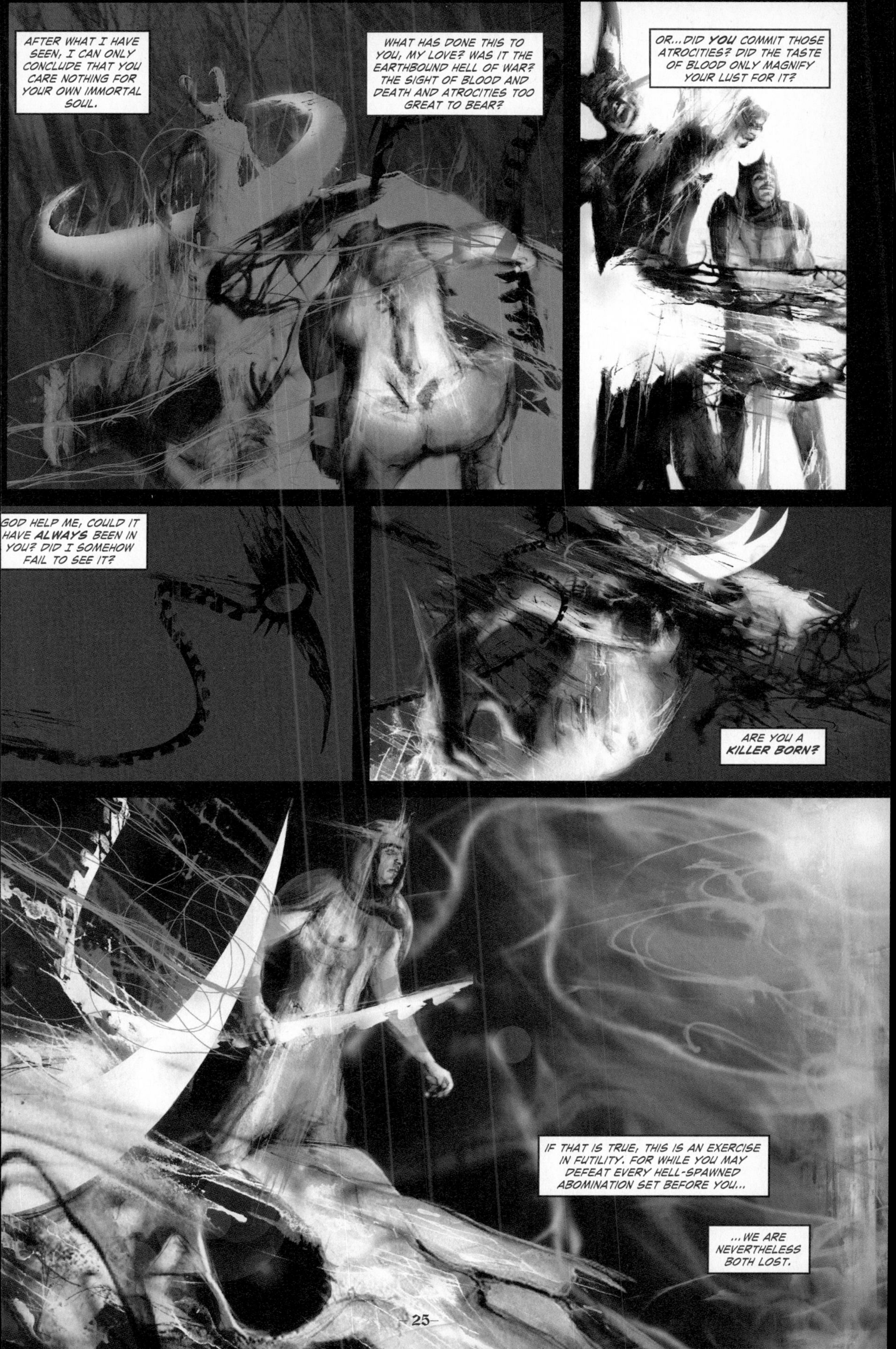
AFTER WHAT I HAVE SEEN, I CAN ONLY CONCLUDE THAT YOU CARE NOTHING FOR YOUR OWN IMMORTAL SOUL.
WHAT HAS DONE THIS TO YOU, MY LOVE? WAS IT THE EARTHBOUND HELL OF WAR? THE SIGHT OF BLOOD AND DEATH AND ATROCITIES TOO GREAT TO BEAR?
OR...DID **YOU** COMMIT THOSE ATROCITIES? DID THE TASTE OF BLOOD ONLY MAGNIFY YOUR LUST FOR IT?
GOD HELP ME, COULD IT HAVE **ALWAYS** BEEN IN YOU? DID I SOMEHOW FAIL TO SEE IT?
ARE YOU A **KILLER BORN?**
IF THAT IS TRUE, THIS IS AN EXERCISE IN FUTILITY. FOR WHILE YOU MAY DEFEAT EVERY HELL-SPAWNED ABOMINATION SET BEFORE YOU...
...WE ARE NEVERTHELESS BOTH LOST.

BUT NO. I MUST HAVE FAITH.
YET MY FAITH IS TEMPERED BY FEAR. FOR WHILE I PRAY THAT YOU MAY YET SAVE OUR SOULS FROM ETERNAL DAMNATION, I MUST ACCEPT THAT, FOR BOTH OF US, THERE IS NO ESCAPING...
...THE FATE OF THE DAMNED.
ARE YOU PREPARED, DANTE?
ARE YOU TRULY PREPARED TO BE JUDGED IN THIS PLACE?

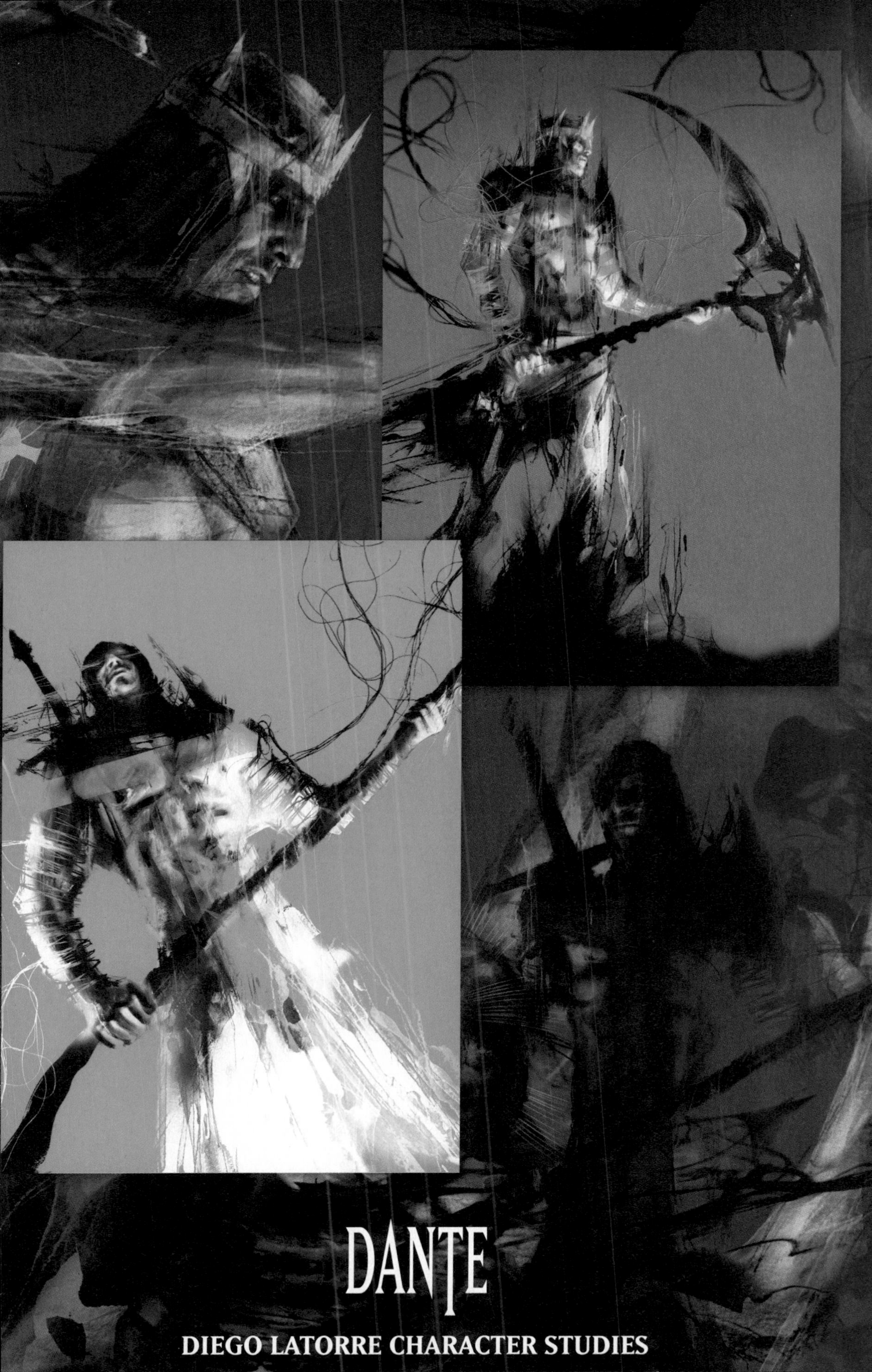
DANTE
DIEGO LATORRE CHARACTER STUDIES

CHAPTER TWO
Descent

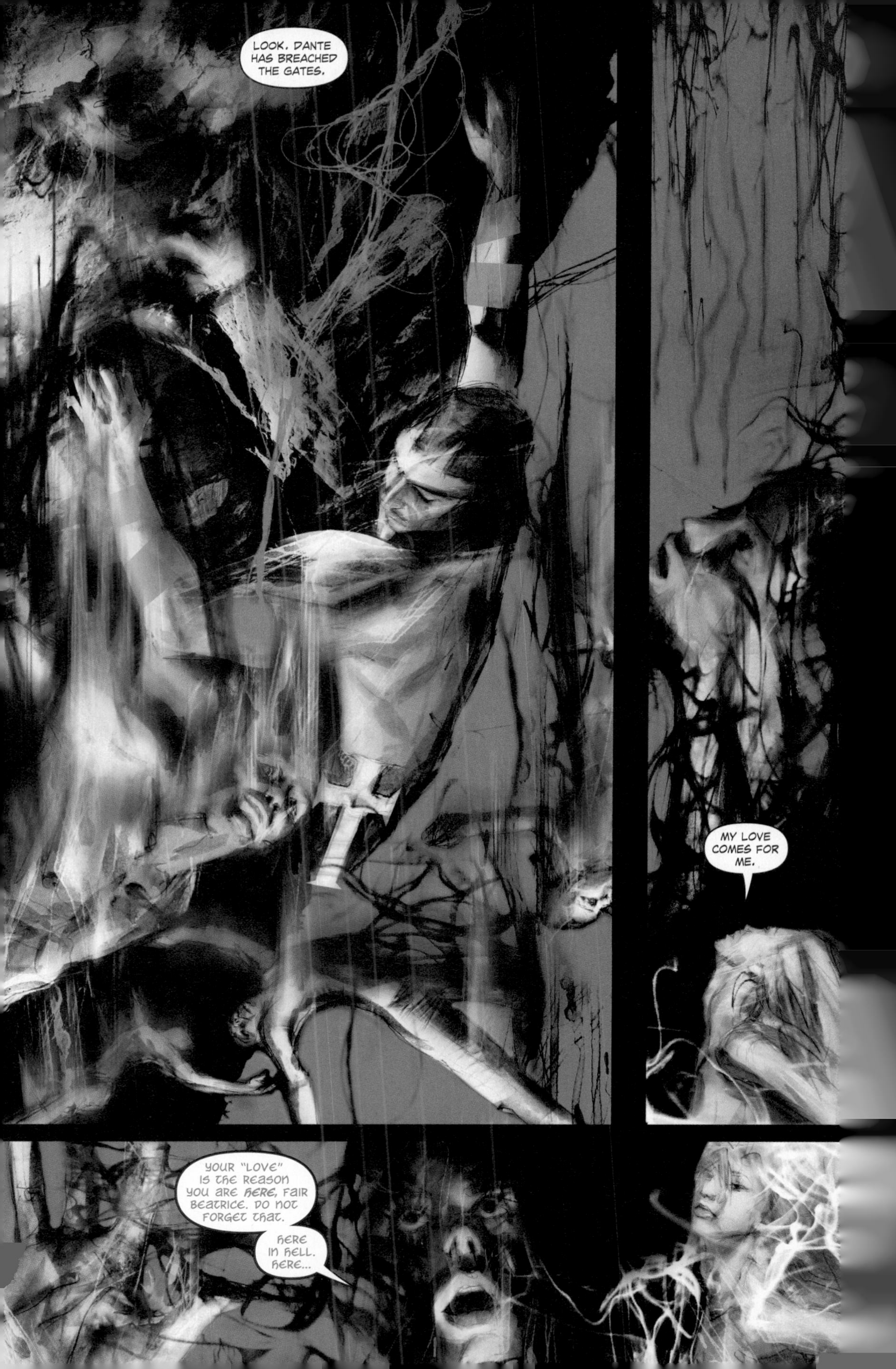
LOOK. DANTE HAS BREACHED THE GATES.
MY LOVE COMES FOR ME.
YOUR "LOVE" IS THE REASON YOU ARE HERE, FAIR BEATRICE. DO NOT FORGET THAT.
HERE IN HELL. HERE...

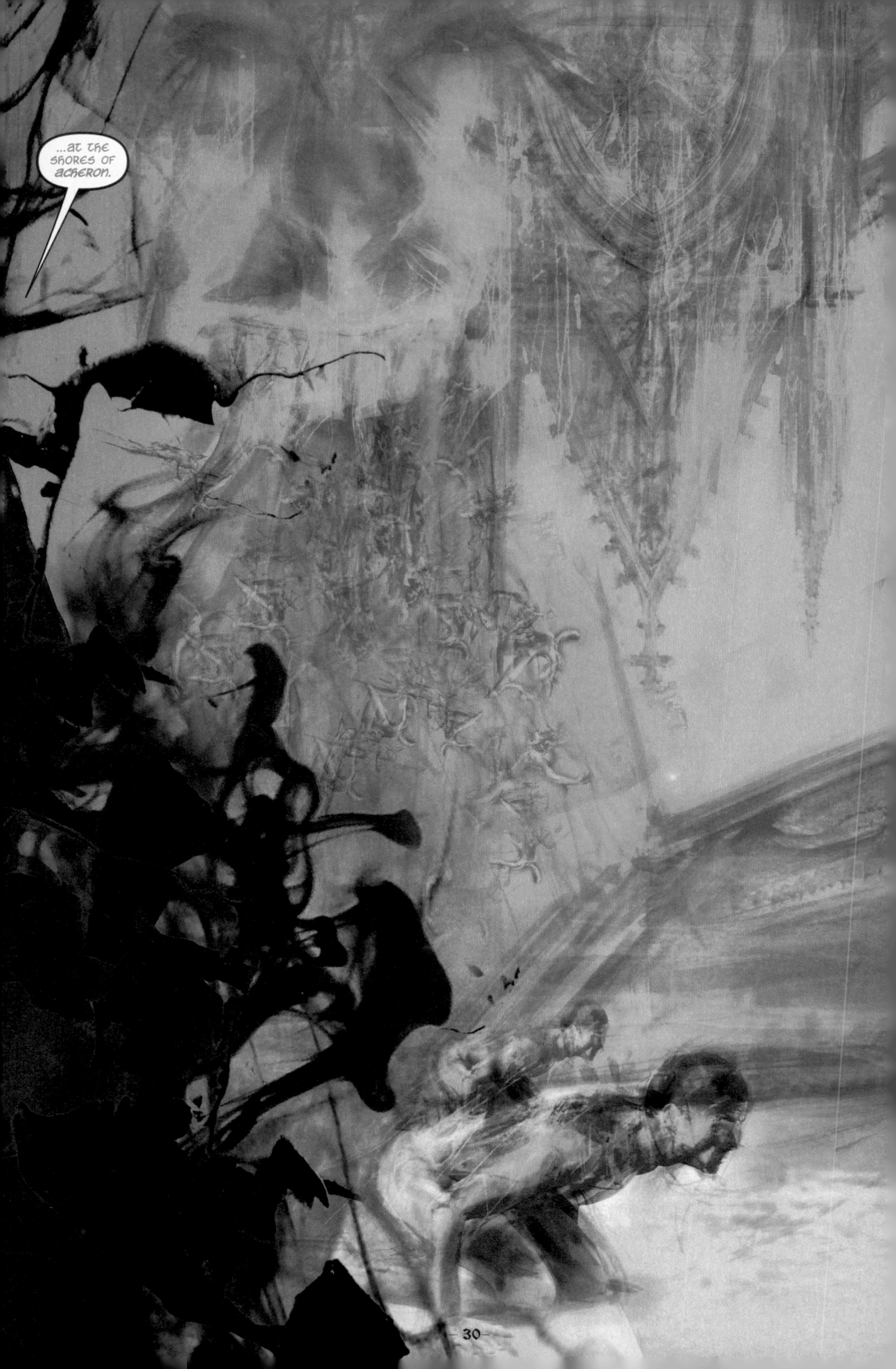
...AT THE SHORES OF ACHERON.

THROUGH ME, THE WAY TO THE CITY OF WOE! THROUGH ME, THE WAY TO EVERLASTING PAIN!
ABANDON ALL HOPE, YE WHO ENTER HERE!

MERCIFUL GOD... THE WATERFALLS. THEY POUR *BODIES.*
NO. *SOULS...* SOULS OF THE DAMNED.
DO NOT TOUCH THEM. WHO KNOWS WHAT PLAGUES INFEST SUCH DEPRAVED SPIRITS?
OFF! DAMNED SHADES, MAKE WAY!
CLEAR A PLACE FOR MY LORD AND HIS BRIDE!

BRIDE? I ASSUMED I WAS SIMPLY BEING CONSIGNED TO HELL.
YOU THOUGHT *ALL* THE DEAD RECEIVE A PERSONAL ESCORT FROM LUCIFER? NO, MY LADY. WHEN YOU LOST OUR WAGER, YOU PLEDGED YOURSELF TO ME.
YOU WERE PLANNING A WEDDING, AND A WEDDING YOU SHALL HAVE. THOUGH THERE HAVE BEEN SOME... *IMPROVEMENTS* TO THE GROOM.

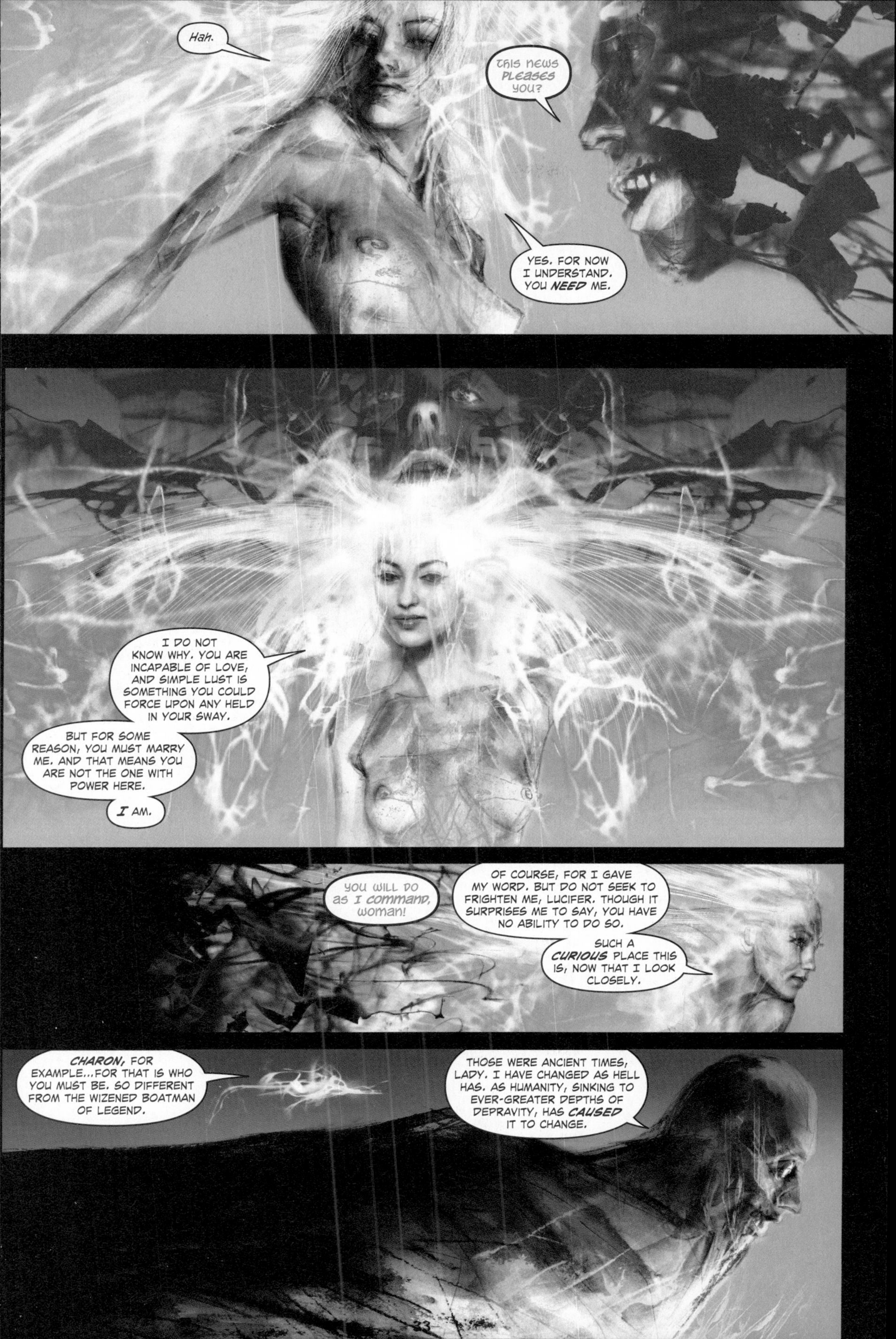
Hah.
THIS NEWS PLEASES YOU?
YES. FOR NOW I UNDERSTAND. YOU NEED ME.
I DO NOT KNOW WHY. YOU ARE INCAPABLE OF LOVE, AND SIMPLE LUST IS SOMETHING YOU COULD FORCE UPON ANY HELD IN YOUR SWAY.
BUT FOR SOME REASON, YOU MUST MARRY ME. AND THAT MEANS YOU ARE NOT THE ONE WITH POWER HERE.
I AM.
YOU WILL DO AS I COMMAND, WOMAN!
OF COURSE, FOR I GAVE MY WORD. BUT DO NOT SEEK TO FRIGHTEN ME, LUCIFER. THOUGH IT SURPRISES ME TO SAY, YOU HAVE NO ABILITY TO DO SO.
SUCH A CURIOUS PLACE THIS IS, NOW THAT I LOOK CLOSELY.
CHARON, FOR EXAMPLE...FOR THAT IS WHO YOU MUST BE. SO DIFFERENT FROM THE WIZENED BOATMAN OF LEGEND.
THOSE WERE ANCIENT TIMES, LADY. I HAVE CHANGED AS HELL HAS. AS HUMANITY, SINKING TO EVER-GREATER DEPTHS OF DEPRAVITY, HAS CAUSED IT TO CHANGE.

HOW TERRIBLE FOR YOU.
I WILL PRAY FOR YOUR BURDEN TO BE LIFTED, CHARON.
I...
...WE HAVE REACHED THE FAR SHORE. I CAN SPEAK...
...NO MORE.
YOUR HABIT OF SPEAKING TO UNDERLINGS IS UNSEEMLY. I CAN SEE MANY LESSONS WILL HAVE TO BE TAUGHT YOU.
FIRST AMONG THEM, THAT YOUR PRAYERS ARE AS USELESS HERE AS THEY WERE ON EARTH.

BEHOLD. IS THAT NOT A FAMILIAR PRESENCE? SOMEONE YOU PRAYED FOR DAILY?

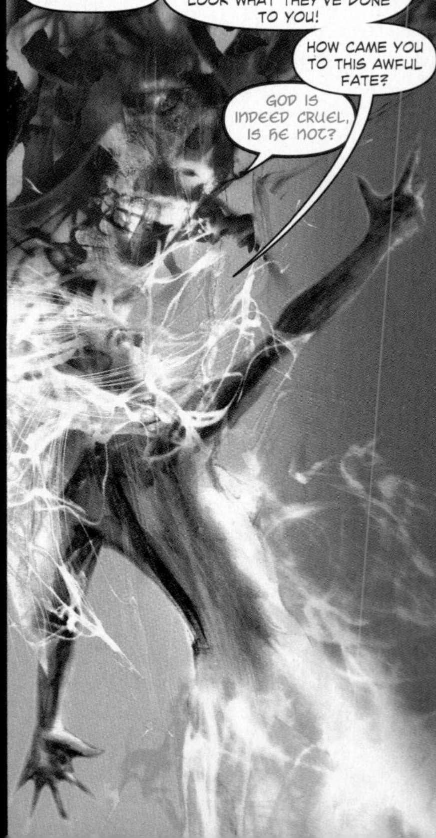
FRANCESCO?
OH, NO...MY POOR BROTHER... LOOK WHAT THEY'VE DONE TO YOU!
HOW CAME YOU TO THIS AWFUL FATE?
GOD IS INDEED CRUEL, IS HE NOT?

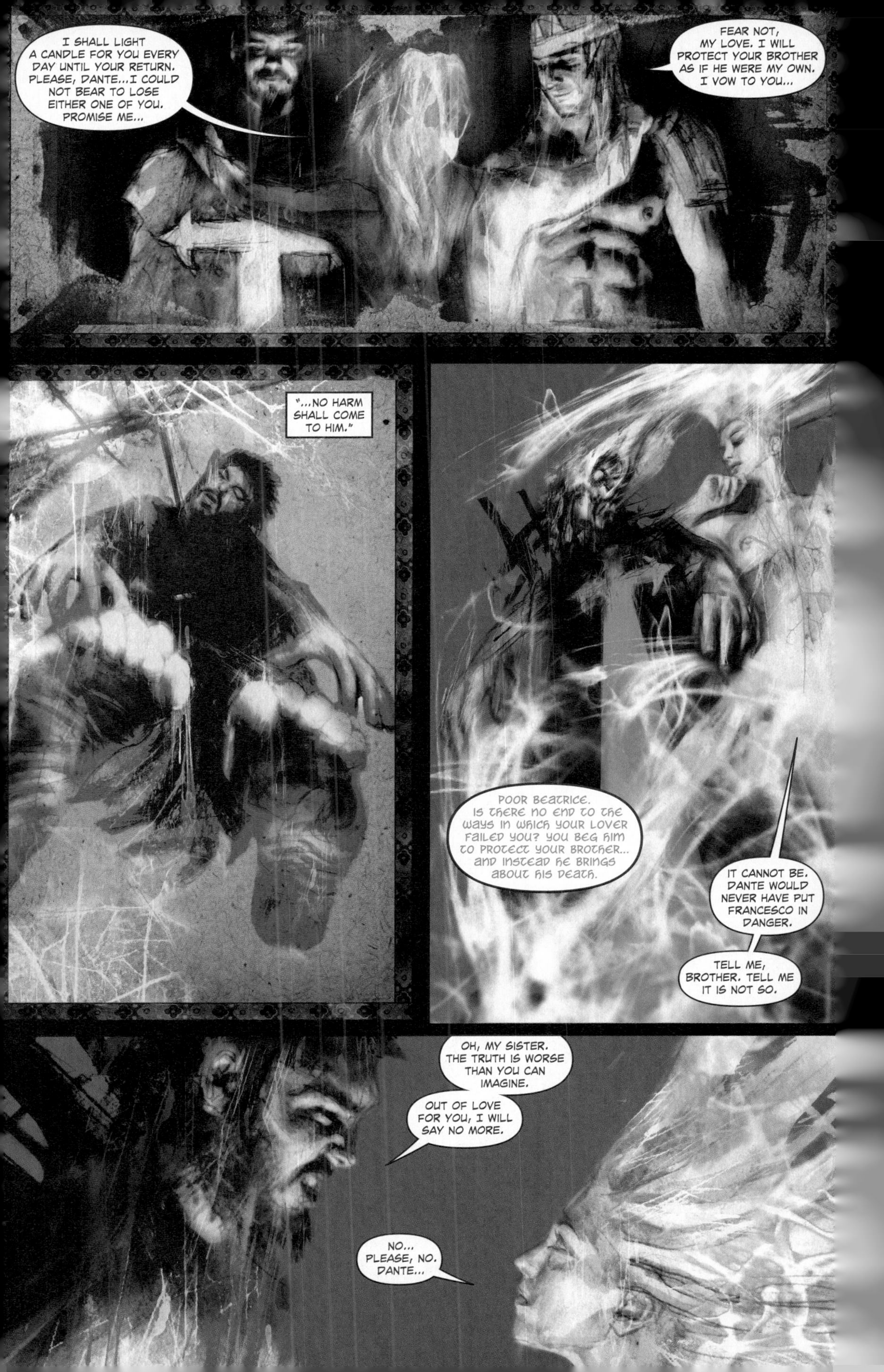
I SHALL LIGHT A CANDLE FOR YOU EVERY DAY UNTIL YOUR RETURN. PLEASE, DANTE...I COULD NOT BEAR TO LOSE EITHER ONE OF YOU. PROMISE ME...
FEAR NOT, MY LOVE. I WILL PROTECT YOUR BROTHER AS IF HE WERE MY OWN. I VOW TO YOU...
"...NO HARM SHALL COME TO HIM."
POOR BEATRICE. IS THERE NO END TO THE WAYS IN WHICH YOUR LOVER FAILED YOU? YOU BEG HIM TO PROTECT YOUR BROTHER... AND INSTEAD HE BRINGS ABOUT HIS DEATH.
IT CANNOT BE. DANTE WOULD NEVER HAVE PUT FRANCESCO IN DANGER.
TELL ME, BROTHER. TELL ME IT IS NOT SO.
OH, MY SISTER. THE TRUTH IS WORSE THAN YOU CAN IMAGINE.
OUT OF LOVE FOR YOU, I WILL SAY NO MORE.
NO... PLEASE, NO. DANTE...

"...WHY HAVE YOU FORSAKEN ME?"
INTERLOPER! STAND ASIDE FROM THOSE THAT ARE DEAD.
WHERE IS BEATRICE?
SHE MADE A VERY FOOLISH WAGER.
TAKE ME TO HER! MY LIFE, MY SOUL FOR HER RETURN!

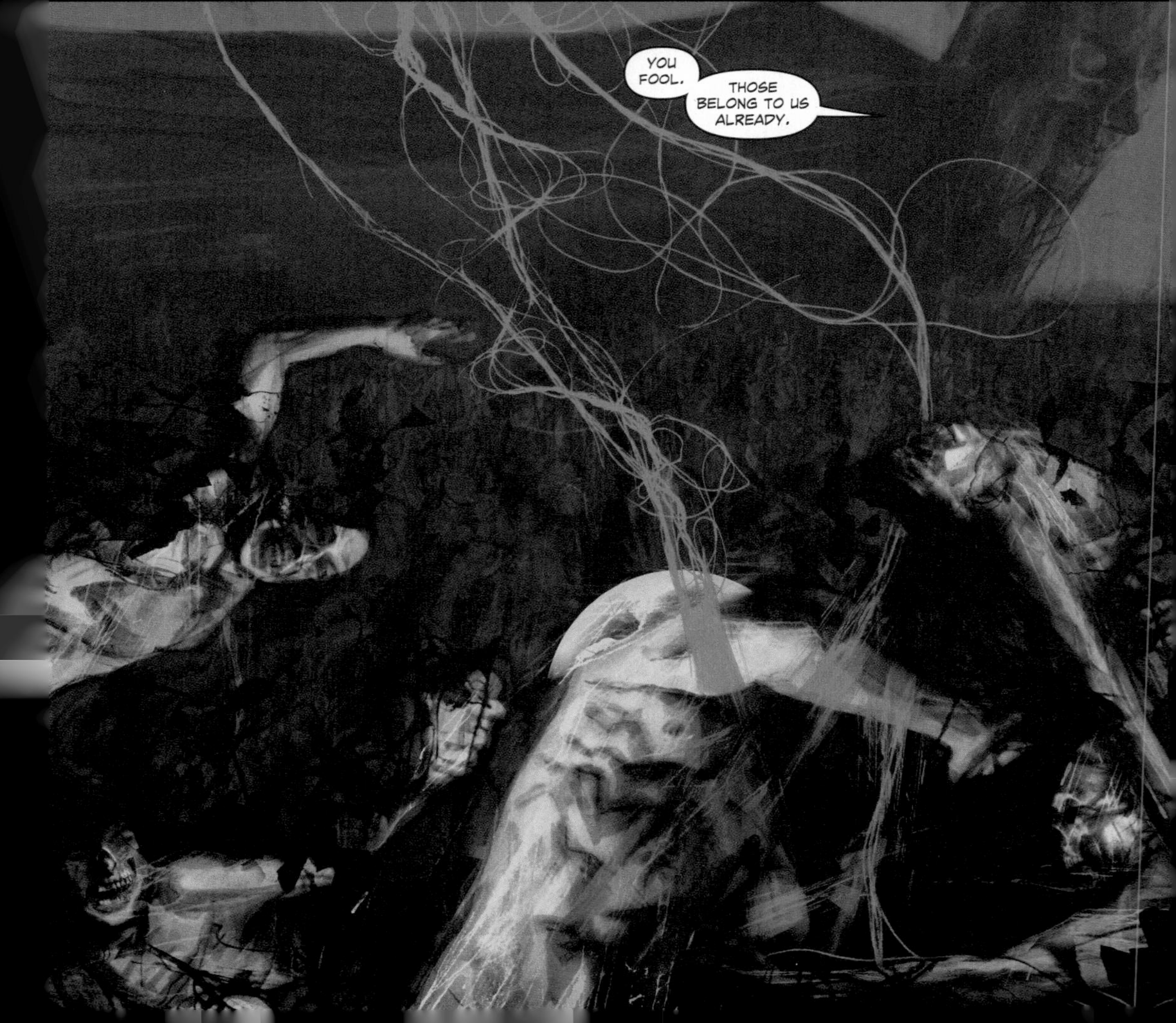
YOU FOOL.
THOSE BELONG TO US ALREADY.

WOE TO YOU, WICKED SOULS! DO NOT HOPE TO EVER SEE PARADISE!
NOW SHALL I FERRY YOU INTO THE FIRE, THE COLD, AND THE ETERNAL, EVERLASTING DARKNESS!
YOU HAVE CONSIGNED YOUR LAST SOUL TO DAMNATION, BOATMAN.
ONLY ONE REMAINS TO DELIVER...

...YOUR OWN!

I SCARCELY... BELIEVE IT. EVEN HERE...HER PRAYER WAS HEARD.
AT LONG LAST... MY BURDEN IS LIFTED.
THANK YOU, LADY BEATRICE.
FOR THE FIRST TIME...
...HELL HAS KNOWN MERCY.

A COMMOTION, BEHIND US--
NOTHING THAT CONCERNS YOU. FOR WE HAVE ARRIVED AT THE ENTRANCE TO YOUR NEW HOME. WELCOME, DEAR BEATRICE, TO THE FIRST CIRCLE OF HELL...
...LIMBO.
Gih?
Ccooo...

Ma...ma...?
WHAT HORROR...?
UNBAPTIZED BABIES. DIED BEFORE THEY TRULY LIVED, CONSIGNED TO THE PIT THROUGH NO FAULT OF THEIR OWN.
I, TOO, AM MYSTIFIED BY HOW YOUR GOD OF LOVE COULD ALLOW SUCH A THING. BUT I DO NOT MAKE THE RULES.
I MERELY ENFORCE THEM. WITH THE AID OF MY OBEDIENT MINIONS... SUCH AS MINOS.
LUST...
...TRAITOR...
...HERETIC...
...MURDERER...
...GLUTTON...

>sniff<... SUICIDE.

IT DOES NOT SURPRISE ME THAT THE ONE WHO PERFORMS THIS HORRIFIC SORTING IS BLIND. NONE WHO CAN SEE WOULD INFLICT SUCH PAIN.
YOUR NAIVETÉ IS CHARMING. IN HELL, MY DEAR, SUCH CONSIDERATIONS MEAN NOTHING. THERE COULD BE NO OTHER OUTCOME. I GRANT YOU, IT MAY GET MESSY AT TIMES...
AIIEE! NO, PLEASE...

...BUT SOULS HAVE A WAY OF ENDING UP WHERE THEY BELONG.
...NOOOOO...

"and we most definitely have a place for your Dante."
WHO COMES INTO MY HOUSE OF PAIN?
ONE WHO LOVES BEATRICE. TELL ME WHERE TO FIND HER.
sniff... I SMELL ONLY A TRAITOR, A GLUTTON, A MURDERER.
WELCOME HOME, SINNER.

SNIFF AGAIN.

LOOK AT HIM, BEATRICE. THE SAVAGE GLEE WITH WHICH HE FIGHTS.
THE *PLEASURE* HE TAKES IN IT.

"THE SAME PLEASURE WE SAW ON THE BATTLEFIELD, AS HE SLAUGHTERED WOMEN AND CHILDREN."

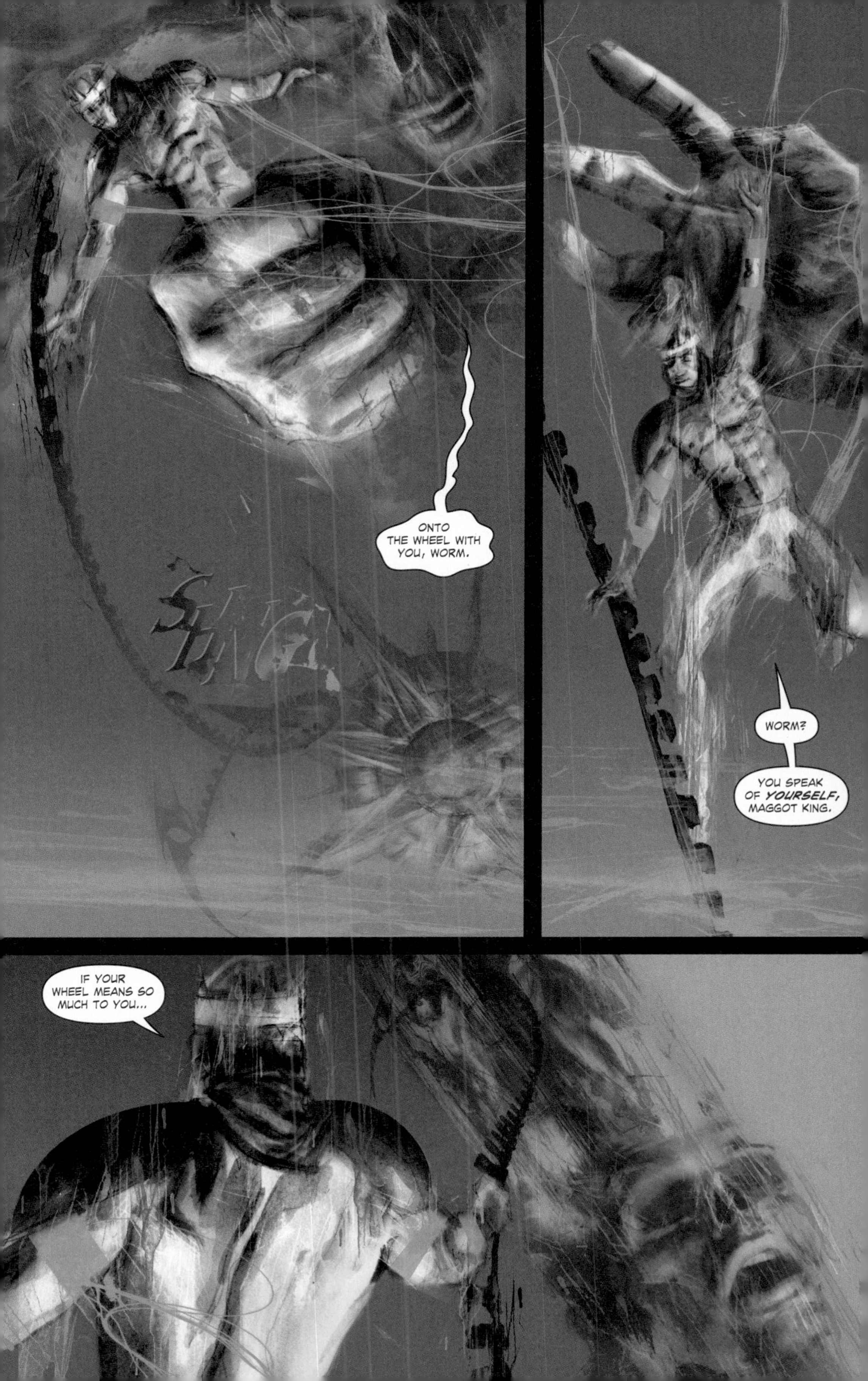
ONTO THE WHEEL WITH YOU, WORM.
WORM?
YOU SPEAK OF ***YOURSELF,*** MAGGOT KING.
IF YOUR WHEEL MEANS SO MUCH TO YOU...

...TASTE IT YOURSELF!
GRAAAGH!
NOW, MONSTER...
...IT'S TIME YOU WERE JUDGED.

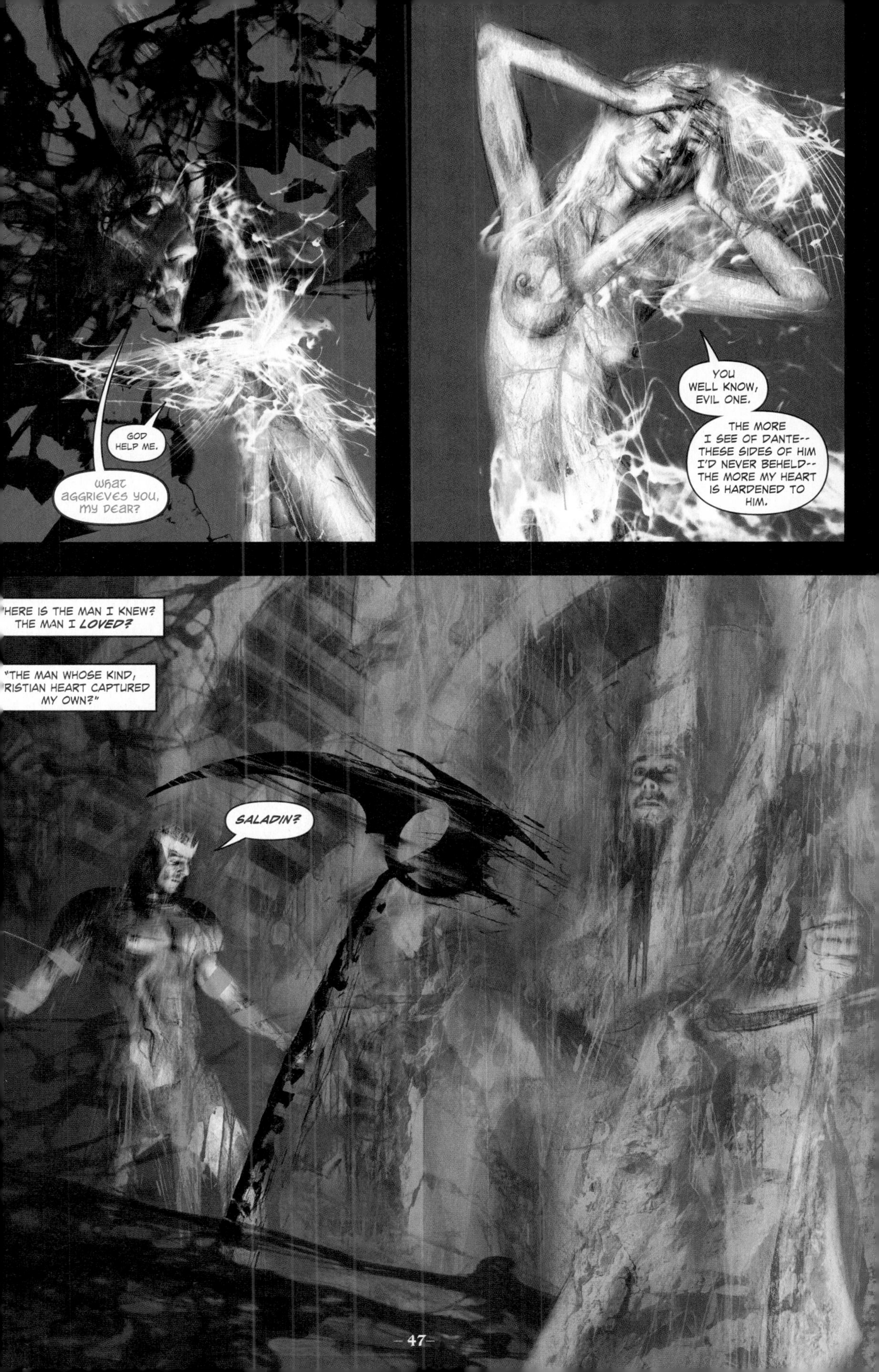
GOD HELP ME.
WHAT AGGRIEVES YOU, MY DEAR?
YOU WELL KNOW, EVIL ONE.
THE MORE I SEE OF DANTE-- THESE SIDES OF HIM I'D NEVER BEHELD-- THE MORE MY HEART IS HARDENED TO HIM.
"HERE IS THE MAN I KNEW? THE MAN I LOVED?
"THE MAN WHOSE KIND, RISTIAN HEART CAPTURED MY OWN?"
SALADIN?

YOU ARE HE, ARE YOU NOT? THE GREAT KURD LEADER WHO RECLAIMED THE HOLY CITY FOR HIS PEOPLE, FROM WHOM EVEN THE BRAVE LIONHEART COULD NOT WREST IT BACK.
HOW DO YOU KNOW ME, STRANGER?
I FOUGHT YOUR ARMIES IN THE CRUSADES. I BEHELD YOU ONCE, FROM A DISTANCE.
AH. FOR ALL THE GOOD OUR BATTLES DID US.
HOW CAME YOU HERE, CHRISTIAN? I WAS TOLD YOUR BISHOPS ABSOLVED YOU SOLDIERS OF ALL SINS...BOTH PAST, AND ANY YOU MIGHT COMMIT IN THE WAR.
WAS I MISLED?

"I...
"...PERHAPS WE WERE ***BOTH*** MISLED AS TO WHAT GOD TRULY WANTS FROM US.

AND YET... YOU WERE RESPECTED, CELEBRATED FOR YOUR HONOR AND CHIVALRY, EVEN AMONG WE WHO OPPOSED YOU. EVEN BY RICHARD LIONHEART HIMSELF.
IT SEEMS UNJUST THAT YOU ARE HERE. WERE IT IN MY POWER, I WOULD ABSOLVE YOU...
WHAT--?
IT SEEMS YOU HAVE POWER YOU DID NOT KNOW OF, MY FRIEND.
I AM FREED FROM THIS PLACE.
CARRY MY STRENGTH WITH YOU ON YOUR QUEST, WARRIOR, AND MAY GOD BE WITH YOU...
"GOD GIVE ME STRENGTH. I MUST BELIEVE MY DANTE STILL EXISTS.
"FOR IF I ACCEPT HIM AS THE UNREPENTANT KILLER I HAVE SEEN...IF I ALLOW MY LOVE FOR HIM TO DIE...
"...WE ARE BOTH LOST."

YOU ARE ALREADY LOST.
FORGET YOUR PRECIOUS DANTE. HE IS OF NO CONSEQUENCE TO US NOW.
WE HAVE MANY PLANS TO MAKE.

FOR SOON THERE SHALL BE A WEDDING. SOON YOU SHALL BE...
...QUEEN OF HELL.

CHAPTER THREE
Debauchery

WELL, MY LORD LUCIFER? WHAT DO YOU THINK OF YOUR BRIDE?
AH. YOU HAVE DONE WELL, CLEOPATRA.
NOW, LADY BEATRICE... *NOW* YOU STRIKE A FITTING FIGURE FOR THE QUEEN OF HELL.
SEE FOR YOURSELF, YOUNG BEATRICE. ARE YOU NOT BEAUTIFUL?
PERHAPS WE'VE TAKEN LIBERTIES DRESSING YOU IN WHITE. BUT COME NOW, HOW MANY OF US ARE REALLY VIRGINS ON OUR WEDDING DAY?
NOT MANY IN *THIS* PLACE, I ASSURE YOU.

AND YET I SENSE YOUR CARNAL KNOWLEDGE IS LIMITED. FEAR NOT, DEAR. I'LL TELL YOU *ALL* THE SECRETS OF SATISFYING YOUR MAN ON YOUR WEDDING NIGHT.
WHY, MY CHILD, TEARS ALREADY? I HAVEN'T EVEN BEGUN!
DANTE...
DO NOT CONCERN YOURSELF WITH YOUR FORMER FLAME.
YOU MAY BE LOST TO HIM, BUT I WILL SEE TO IT HE HAS ALL THE COMPANIONSHIP HE NEEDS HERE IN THE SECOND CIRCLE...

...THE REALM OF LUST.

"AND IF HE INSISTS ON SEEING YOU...WELL.
"YOU ARE HARDLY THE DEMURE MAIDEN HE LEFT BEHIND, ARE YOU?"
WHAT NEW OBSTACLE--? NO. IT DOES NOT MATTER.
DEMONS...LUCIFER HIMSELF...
...NOTHING CAN KEEP ME FROM YOU, MY LOVE.
I AM COMING, BEATRICE!
AND NOTHING CAN STAND...
...IN MY... WAY...
AND WHY SHOULD WE, DANTE? WE'VE WAITED SO LONG FOR A HANDSOME, POWERFUL HERO.
COME TO US, DANTE. WE ACHE FOR YOUR TOUCH. YOUR STRONG, COMMANDING ARMS.
I... WILL NOT. I CANNOT... CANNOT...
...I...CANNOT RESIST...

WHERE HAVE YOU TAKEN ME, WITCHES? WHERE...
...BEATRICE? I SCARCELY RECOGNIZE YOU...
NOR SHOULD YOU. I AM NOT THE WOMAN YOU KNEW. WHEN I AM WED TO LUCIFER, I SHALL BE OF THIS PLACE... FOREVERMORE.
BEATRICE, DON'T DO THIS.
BECAUSE OF YOU, I MUST.
I WOULD NEVER DO ANYTHING TO CONDEMN YOU TO SUCH A FATE.
BUT YOU DID.
DECEIVER! RELEASE HER, I DEMAND IT!
DECEIVER? I?
MOST UNGRACIOUS OF YOU, SIR. I HAVE ABIDED BY EVERY BARGAIN I MADE TO LADY BEATRICE. YOU, ON THE OTHER HAND, SWORE TO BE FOREVER TRUE TO HER.
TO RENOUNCE ALL PLEASURES OF THE FLESH UNTIL YOU RETURNED TO HER.
A VOW SHE BELIEVED IN SO STRONGLY SHE WAGERED HER IMMORTAL SOUL THAT YOU HAD KEPT IT.
LET US SEE HOW THAT TURNED OUT, SHALL WE?

YOU MUST HAVE MISHEARD, FRANCESCO. WHY WOULD KING RICHARD WANT US TO BABYSIT THREE THOUSAND FLEA-RIDDEN PRISONERS? TO WHAT END?
HE INTENDS TO USE THEM TO NEGOTIATE WITH SALADIN. THEIR FREEDOM IN EXCHANGE FOR THE RETURN OF THE TRUE CROSS.
NEGOTIATE? WITH HERETICS? IMPOSSIBLE.
ALL THAT WILL ACCOMPLISH IS TO FURTHER DELAY OUR RETURN HOME.
HAVEN'T WE SUFFERED **ENOUGH** ON THIS DAMNABLE CRUSADE? HAVEN'T ***I*** SUFFERED ENOUGH?
A MOMENT, CHRISTIAN. THERE'S ***NO NEED*** FOR YOUR SUFFERING.
I CAN COMFORT YOU. ***AND*** I ***WILL...*** IF YOU LET MY BROTHER GO.
I HAVE A WOMAN, IN FLORENCE.
AND HOW LONG HAS IT BEEN SINCE YOU SAW HER? SINCE YOU FELT HER CARESS? HOW DO YOU KNOW YOU'LL EVER SEE HER AGAIN?
DANTE, DON'T--
UNHAND ME.
YOUR SISTER IS AN OCEAN AWAY. SAFE FROM THE HORRORS OF THIS PLACE...OF THIS WAR. AND I WOULD HAVE IT NO OTHER WAY.
BUT ***I*** AM ***HERE.*** AND BEATRICE CANNOT COMFORT ME FROM FLORENCE.
SO I SHALL TAKE WHAT SUCCOR I CAN FIND...WHERE I MAY FIND IT.
LET ME MAKE YOU FORGET HER. FORGET YOUR PAIN... YOUR FEAR...YOUR LONELINESS.

WELL, CHRISTIAN? ARE YOU COMFORTED?
IN TRUTH? MORE TROUBLED THAN BEFORE. BUT IT'S NO FAULT OF YOURS. YOU WERE MOST... ACCOMMODATING. I TRUST I WAS AS WELL.
YOU WERE GENTLE.
I'M NO BRUTE.
NO. YOU DID NOT TAKE MY LIFE.
ONLY MY HONOR. ONLY THE HONOR OF MY BROTHER, OF OUR FAMILY. ONLY ANY HAPPINESS I MAY HAVE EVER HOPED TO FIND IN THIS WORLD.
YOU HAVE DONE FAR WORSE THAN SLAY ME, INFIDEL. TO SAVE MY BROTHER, YOU HAVE MADE ME DEBASE MYSELF. MADE ME A WHORE.
THE TRUTH IS NOT SO PLEASING TO YOUR EARS AS MY EARLIER HONEYED WORDS? I DON'T CARE! WE HAD A BARGAIN! I KEPT MY PART, NOW KEEP YOURS!
SHOW A SMALL PIECE OF THE MERCY YOU FOLLOWERS OF CHRIST CLAIM TO HOLD SO DEAR! SET MY BROTHER FREE!
GUARDS! RELEASE THIS ONE. HER BROTHER AS WELL.
I DO NOT WISH TO SEE EITHER OF THEM. EVER AGAIN.
BEATRICE... WHAT HAVE I DONE...
HER BROTHER... IS THE MAN WHO KILLED YOU. WHO SLEW BOTH OUR FAMILIES.
I...IT WAS NEVER MY INTENTION TO...
INTENTIONS SUCH AS YOURS PAVE THE WAY TO MY REALM, DEAR DANTE!

WHY MAKE A PROMISE YOU CAN'T KEEP? WHY, DANTE?
YOU DON'T KNOW WHAT IT WAS LIKE!
AH, BUT SHE DOES. I SHOWED HER.
DANTE...IS RIGHT. I CANNOT POSSIBLY COMPREHEND WHAT HE FELT IN THOSE YEARS. THE LONELINESS... THE FEAR...THE DEATH...
THEY DO NOT JUSTIFY HIS BETRAYAL.
TRUE. HE TURNED HIS BACK ON OUR LOVE. AND I SHOULD HATE HIM FOR IT.
BUT I ONLY FEEL EMPTINESS.
ENOUGH. WE HAVE A WEDDING TO PERFORM.
NO!
FEAR NOT, DANTE. A LADIES' MAN SUCH AS YOURSELF WILL APPRECIATE THE LEGENDARY BEAUTY TO WHOSE TENDER MERCIES I LEAVE YOU.
OF COURSE, HELL CHANGES ALL WHO ENTER...
...EVEN CLEOPATRA.

LET ME SLAY HIM FOR YOU, MISTRESS!
I NEVER COULD REFUSE YOU, ANTONY. HAVE AT THE FOOL.
A FOOL INDEED HAVE I BEEN. BUT I PALE IN COMPARISON TO YOU.
OH? YOU, WHO GAVE UP THE KINGDOM OF HEAVEN--NOT JUST FOR YOURSELF, BUT FOR YOUR ONE TRUE LOVE--ALL FOR THE TITS OF A SLAVE GIRL?
PRAY TELL, HOW CAN ANYONE TOP THAT?
I DID NOT AGREE TO SERVE LUCIFER.
I DID NOT SEND MY TRUE LOVE INTO BATTLE...

...AGAINST A MAN FIGHTING FOR SALVATION!
ANTONY! NO!!
THIS CANNOT BE. I CANNOT STAY IN THIS PLACE ALONE...
...WAIT. HIS SOUL. IT FINDS REFUGE IN YOU, DANTE.
IN YOU!
YOU SHALL TAKE HIS PLACE. YOU SHALL BE MINE.
COME TO ME!
I COME...

...PREPARE TO RECEIVE ME!
...GOODBYE... MY LOVE...
...FORGIVE ME...
BEATRICE...

...FORGIVE ME!
I DO. I FORGIVE HIM.
DANTE CANNOT HELP SUCCUMBING TO HIS BASER INSTINCTS. HE HAD NO OTHER EXAMPLE.
"AS CHILDREN, WE SPIED UPON THE FEASTS THROWN BY LORD ALIGHIERO AND LADY BELLA.
"ENOUGH TO FEED THE STARVING PEASANTRY FOR A YEAR WAS WASTED AND CAST ASIDE...
"...BUT WOE BETIDE ANY SERVANT GIRL WHO DARED ATTEMPT TO TAKE THE TABLE SCRAPS FOR HER FAMILY.

"OR WHO VENTURED TOO CLOSE TO ALIGHIERO'S QUESTING HANDS... INCURRING HIS LUST AND HIS LADY'S WRATH."

LOOK AT ME THAT WAY MUCH LONGER, BOY, AND I'LL TAKE YOU OVER MY KNEE.
WHO MADE YOU A PRIEST? HAHAHA!

WHO MADE YOU A PRIEST? EITHER JOIN US, FRANCESCO, OR BEGONE.
"A CHILD IS SHAPED BY HIS PARENTS. DANTE STRUGGLES ETERNALLY TO REJECT THEIR WAYS. IT IS A BATTLE HE MAY NOT ALWAYS WIN...
"...BUT AS LONG AS HE FIGHTS IT, THERE IS HOPE."
EXCREMENT. EMPTY, FALSE WORDS EVEN YOU CANNOT BELIEVE.
YOUR PRECIOUS GOD GAVE HUMANITY FREE WILL. HIS GREATEST BLESSING. WHEN ANGELS LIKE MYSELF PROTESTED YOU WERE NOT WORTHY OF IT--
--HE CAST US OUT OF HEAVEN! CHOOSING YOU OVER US! AND WHAT DO YOU DO WITH YOUR PRECIOUS GIFT? DENY IT AT EVERY TURN! "THE DEVIL MADE ME DO IT."
HAH!
"THE ACTIONS OF HIS ELDERS MEAN NOTHING. DANTE IS HIS OWN MAN.
"HE CHOSE HIS FATE.

"IT IS ON HIS HEAD ALONE IF HE NOW REAPS THE CONSEQUENCES...

"...OF HIS
GLUTTONY.

"But forget him. It is no longer your concern what fate his sins have brought him to...
...but rather, where they have brought you.
Your wedding day.

OH!
THE... THE ENTIRE STRUCTURE IS MADE OF...
Nnuhh...
...ohhh...
SHADES, YES. MAKING THEMSELVES USEFUL, AS FEW DID IN LIFE.
THAT IS THE NATURE OF OUR KINGDOM, MY DEAR. IT'S NOT I WHO MAKES HELL WHAT IT IS...BUT RATHER THE SINNERS THEMSELVES.
"THINK ON THAT, AND TAKE A MOMENT TO BID YOUR OLD LIFE FAREWELL, WHILE I VISIT ONE SINNER IN PARTICULAR...
"...WHO COULD CHANGE THE VERY LANDSCAPE OF HELL...

"...IF THEY PLAY THEIR PARTS CORRECTLY.

WHY DO YOU FIGHT SO, DANTE? CAN YOU NOT ACCEPT THAT YOU HAVE COME HOME?
NO. I DO *NOT* BELONG HERE.
I FOUGHT IN THE CRUSADE! THE BISHOP ABSOLVED US OF OUR SINS!
HA! THAT SALESMAN OF SALVATION? AND YOU BELIEVED HIM?
PERHAPS YOU CAN REGISTER YOUR COMPLAINT PERSONALLY, SOON ENOUGH.
AND WHAT OF THE HEATHENS WE KILLED? WHERE ARE THEY?
THEY THOUGHT THEIR CAUSE HOLY, TOO. PERHAPS *THEY* WERE RIGHT, AND *YOU* WERE THE INFIDEL.
NO! I REFUSE TO ACCEPT THAT!
ANSWER ME, LUCIFER! WHY DO I NOT FIND *THEM* DAMNED HERE?

BECAUSE, DANTE, THIS ISN'T THEIR HELL...
...IT'S YOURS.
...NO...

NO!!

PERHAPS YOU ARE RIGHT. THE THIRD CIRCLE WAS NOT FOR YOU. GLUTTONY WAS MORE YOUR *FATHER'S* AVOCATION.
SPEAK NOT OF MY FATHER, DEMON.
BUT WHY? YOU HAVE SO MUCH IN COMMON.
LUST, GLUTTONY...THEY ARE ALL SINS OF COVETOUSNESS. OF WANTING.
OF *GREED.*
THAT FIGURE... I RECOGNIZE IT. I...
...NO. IT *CAN'T* BE...
...FATHER?

CLOSE YOUR GAPING MOUTH, BOY.
THE WAY YOU ALWAYS STARED AT ME WITH THAT LOOK OF CONDEMNATION, YOU CAN'T BE SURPRISED TO FIND ME HERE.
Pfah. THEN TURN BACK, COWARD. ACCEPT YOUR FATE AND GO NO FURTHER.
AND YET HERE ***YOU*** ARE AS WELL. ALL YOUR SUPERIOR AIRS AND HOLY CRUSADES GONE TO NAUGHT. TELL ME, DO YOU STILL THINK YOURSELF A BETTER MAN THAN YOUR FATHER?
I THINK I'M TOO MUCH MY FATHER'S SON.
NO. IT IS ***BEATRICE'S*** FATE THAT IS UNDESERVED. I WILL NOT REST UNTIL I HAVE FOUND HER.

THEN WE'LL LEARN ONCE AND FOR ALL WHO'S THE BETTER MAN!

PATHETIC CHILD. SO SELF-RIGHTEOUS... BUT LUCIFER HAS SHOWN ME HOW YOUR SINS DWARF MY OWN!
YET YOU STILL HAVE THE GALL TO BLAME YOUR ACTIONS ON ME? AFTER ALL I GAVE YOU?
GUHH!
ALL... YOU GAVE ME...
...WAS GREED...
...AND HATE!!

I WILL NOT BE DAMNED LIKE YOU!
GRAAAAGH!

YOU... ARE A GROWN MAN, DANTE. PERHAPS I SHAPED... THE MAN YOU BECAME...
...BUT YOU... ARE RESPONSIBLE...
...FOR THE MAN YOU ARE...
...BEATRICE...
BEATRICE!
I WILL SAVE YOU!

AH, MY LOVE...
...I FEAR NO ONE CAN SAVE ME NOW.
FOR THIS UNION, JOINED IN BLOOD...
...FOREVER MAY IT BURN IN THE FIRES OF HELL.

CHAPTER FOUR
DESPAIR

BEATRICE! DON'T DO THIS!
ah, but it's already done, dante.

Lovely beatrice and I are man and wife.
now only the *consummation* remains.
NO!
I VOW BEFORE GOD, LUCIFER, IF YOU TOUCH HER, I'LL--
isn't that always the way? those who were unfaithful themselves show the greatest outrage when their lovers stray.
but I speak not of carnality. we have an eternity for that. I refer, rather, to the thing that will bind beatrice to hell for all time.
take it, my dear. eat. let the pomegranate seeds take root within you...make you *one of us.*

NO!!

I...FEEL ITS POWER. IT PULSES IN MY HANDS.
THIS HESITATION IS UNSEEMLY, FAIR LADY. YOU'VE GIVEN YOUR WORD. TAKEN YOUR VOWS.
IT IS RATHER TOO LATE TO GIVE IN TO YOUR FEARS.

I DO NOT FEAR YOU, LUCIFER...OR THIS PLACE. I FEAR MYSELF.

THE PART OF ME THAT CRAVES THE POWER I SENSE CAN BE MINE. THE THOUGHT THAT I MIGHT GIVE IN TO THE SINS I HAVE WITNESSED HERE...
...TO THE PAIN AND ANGER ROILING WITHIN ME, AFTER LEARNING OF DANTE'S TRANSGRESSIONS.

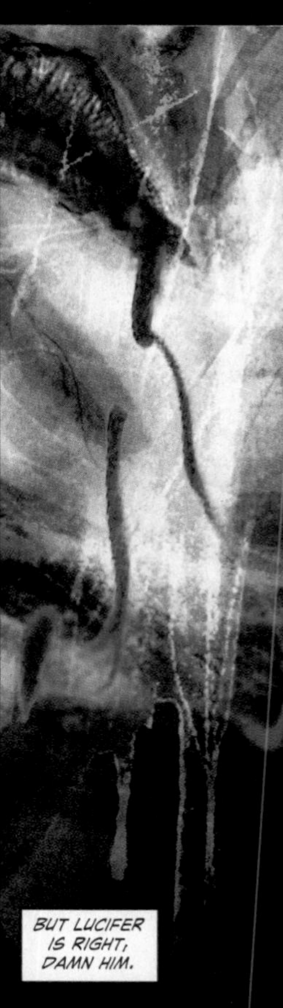
BUT LUCIFER IS RIGHT, DAMN HIM.
I HAVE COME TOO FAR TO TURN BACK NOW.

BEATRICE...
NO. YOUR TRUSTING, INNOCENT BEATRICE IS NO LONGER.
YOUR LOVER IS NOW MY WIFE.
BEHOLD THE QUEEN OF HELL!

WELL, MY QUEEN? DO YOU REGRET YOUR DECISION?
I... NO.
THERE IS NO PAIN. NO FEAR. QUITE THE CONTRARY...IT'S WONDERFUL.
INTOXICATING.
I FEEL STRONGER...MORE PLEASURE THAN I'VE EVER KNOWN. FAR MORE THAN I FELT IN DANTE'S ARMS.
THERE IS A PRICE.
WHAT--?
IGNORE THE LAST PITIFUL MEWLINGS OF YOUR OLD SELF AS IT DIES.

ARE THERE NOT LOUDER VOICES WITHIN YOU? STIRRINGS FAR MORE COMPELLING... FAR EASIER TO GIVE IN TO?
Y-YES.

YES.

BEATRICE! STOP! I'M SORRY!
ALWAYS JUST TOO LATE, AREN'T YOU?
THE FAITHFUL HAS LOST HER FAITH. THE INCORRUPTIBLE HAS BEEN CORRUPTED. THE TRUE INNOCENT HAS GIVEN WAY TO THE SINS OF MAN.
YOU'VE LOST, DANTE. FIND YOUR PROPER CIRCLE AND SUBMIT TO THE ETERNITY OF TORMENT YOU'VE WORKED SO HARD TO EARN.
BEYOND THESE WALLS IS THE SIXTH CIRCLE...DWELLING PLACE OF HERETICS. I BELIEVE THAT WILL DO NICELY.
FOR WASN'T YOUR CRUSADE A LIE AND A HERESY... MUCH LIKE YOUR LIFE?
GOD HELP ME, HE IS RIGHT.
BEATRICE HAS PAID THE ULTIMATE PRICE FOR MY SINS. WHAT PURPOSE IS THERE IN CONTINUING TO FIGHT FATE?
PERHAPS, DANTE, YOU SHOULD NOT GIVE UP...
...BECAUSE BEATRICE HAS NOT YET GIVEN UP ON YOU.
VIRGIL!
RISE. THE FIERY TOMBS OF HERESY AWAIT.
WHERE HAVE YOU BEEN HIDING, POET? YOU SWORE TO GUIDE ME THROUGH THIS INFERNAL REALM!

AND SO I SHALL, WHEN I AM ABLE. BUT I MUST ABIDE BY THE RULES OF THE INFERNO. AS MUST ALL WHO DWELL WITHIN...FROM THE HERETICS THAT SURROUND US TO LUCIFER HIMSELF.
TAKE HEART, DANTE. THE BEATRICE YOU KNEW REMAINS, TRAPPED INSIDE WHAT SHE HAS BECOME. BUT IN TIME SHE WILL FADE...UNLESS YOU RELEASE HER.
DO NOT ABANDON HER. SHE HAS NOT ABANDONED YOU, DESPITE SEEING YOU AT YOUR WORST.
NO...

"...NOT MY WORST."
DANTE, *DON'T!* THEY'RE OUR *PRISONERS--*
WE ARE AS MUCH PRISONERS AS THEY, FRANCESCO!
TRAPPED HERE GUARDING THESE HEATHENS WHO WOULD SLAY US WITHOUT A SECOND THOUGHT...ONLY WHEN THEY'RE *GONE* CAN WE BE RELEASED.
THERE IS NO SHAME IN IT. THEIR SOULS ARE ALREADY DAMNED. THAT IS WHY WE CAME TO THIS LAND, IS IT NOT? TO *KILL HERETICS?*
THEN LET THE LORD'S WORK BE DONE!

AND YET... YOU SPEAK THE TRUTH, VIRGIL.
I DO NOT HAVE THE RIGHT TO SURRENDER BEATRICE TO DAMNATION. NOT WHEN SHE IS HERE BECAUSE OF ME.
I SWEAR BY ALL THAT IS HOLY AND UNHOLY...
...BEATRICE WILL BE FREE!
SKAASH
WELL SPOKEN, DANTE. DO NOT LET YOUR DETERMINATION FADE.
FOR YOUR ENEMIES ASSUREDLY WILL NOT.

THEIR PERSISTENCE BAFFLES ME. I HAVE NO QUARREL WITH THIS MONSTER.
WHAT QUARREL DID YOU HAVE WITH PRISONERS WHOSE NAMES YOU NEVER KNEW? OR THEY WITH YOU?

THE MINOTAUR IS A CREATURE OF VIOLENCE. HE LASHES OUT AT ALL AROUND HIM. UNLIKE SOME, HE DOES NOT PRETEND TO REQUIRE A REASON.
THEN HE IS DOOMED.
HRREEGGH!

FOR I *HAVE* A REASON.
AND NOTHING WILL KEEP ME FROM HER!
FAR BEHIND US...I CAN FEEL HIM.
DANTE COMES. STILL HE COMES...
YOU WISH TO GREET HIM? VERY WELL. HOW CAN I REFUSE MY NEW BRIDE?
GO TO WELCOME HIM. YOU HAVE MY LEAVE...AND MY BLESSING.
BUT LET ME SHOW YOU ONE LAST THING ERE YOU DO...

DAMNATION. EVEN IN WAR I NEVER KNEW SUCH UNCEASING ATTACKS.
CENTAURS. **MORE** CREATURES OF MYTH. BEINGS I THOUGHT DID NOT EXIST.
AND SOON I WILL BE RIGHT.

WAIT, BROTHERS. HOLD YOUR FIRE.
MY APOLOGIES, STRANGER. I TOOK YOU FOR A HERETIC FLEEING THE BOUNDS OF HIS CIRCLE. BUT NOW THAT YOU DRAW CLOSER, I SEE YOU BELONG HERE.
WELCOME, FELLOW MURDERER. YOU WILL FEEL AT HOME IN THIS PLACE, AMONG THE SCREAMS OF FEAR AND AGONY, WHERE ALL HANDS ARE SOAKED WITH BLOOD.

SO MUCH SO, THAT A RIVER OF BOILING BLOOD IS OUR ETERNAL REWARD...
...IN THE DOMAIN OF VIOLENCE.
YOU DO NOT WISH TO BATHE? VERY WELL. WE HAVE THREE RINGS HERE IN THE SEVENTH CIRCLE.
I HAVE NO DOUBT YOU WILL FIND ONE THAT SUITS YOU...

NNGUHH...
WHAT--?
THE TREES-- THEY ARE ALL--
SHADES, YES. THE RIVER OF BOILING BLOOD IS FOR SINNERS WHO HARMED OTHERS. HERE DWELL THOSE WHO COMMITTED VIOLENCE AGAINST THEMSELVES.
HARRIED BY THE HARPIES WHO TEAR AT THEIR BRANCHES, THEY ETERNALLY SUFFER THE PAIN THEY BROKE GOD'S LAW TO ESCAPE. THIS IS THE WOOD OF SUICIDES.
WAIT. IT CAN'T BE.
AWAY! AWAY, FOUL HARPIES!

BEGONE! I MUST KNOW IF MY EYES DECEIVE ME, OR--
--NO. MOTHER...
YOU-- THIS IS UNJUST. YOU DIED OF THE FEVER.
OH, DANTE... MY POOR, GULLIBLE BOY.
"IS THAT WHAT THE BASTARD TOLD YOU?"
HER HEART GAVE OUT, SON. THE FEVER... SHE WAS TOO WEAK.
"YES. I WAS WEAK. TOO WEAK TO STAND UP TO HIS BRUTALITY...
"...AND TOO WEAK TO ENDURE IT ANY FURTHER.

AND YOU... YOU LEARNED HIS WAYS.
MOTHER...
FORGIVE ME.
DANTE, THE FAULT IS *MINE.* I LACKED THE COURAGE TO STAY. TO PROTECT YOU.
CAN YOU FORGIVE *ME?*
HOW CAN I NOT, WHEN I HAVE SUCCUMBED TO MY OWN WEAKNESS AT EVERY TURN?
I WOULD ABSOLVE YOU, MOTHER. I WOULD HAVE YOU KNOW PEACE...
MY BELOVED SON. MY SOUL HAS ALWAYS BELONGED TO YOU...AND NOW IT TRULY SHALL.
MAY I GIVE YOU THE STRENGTH IN DEATH I COULD NOT IN LIFE.
WAIT. MOTHER, DO YOU MEAN--THE SOULS I ABSOLVED ARE *PART* OF ME?

THROUGH THE CROSS, YES. AS YOU DEPEND ON THEM, DANTE, SO THEY DEPEND ON YOU. THEIR REDEMPTION IS TIED TO YOUR OWN...AS IS BEATRICE'S INNOCENT SPIRIT.
BUT TO SAVE US ALL, YOU MUST FACE YOUR OWN SINS AND CONQUER THEM. YOU WILL HAVE TO BE STRONG, MY SON...STRONGER THAN EVER BEFORE...
...FOR ONLY THE STRONGEST CAN FACE THE DARKNESS IN THEIR HEARTS...

YOU KNEW? AND YOU DIDN'T--
I TOLD YOU THERE WAS BUT ONE WAY TO FIND STRENGTH IN HELL. AND THAT IT WAS NOT FOR ME TO REVEAL.
YOU HAVE DISCOVERED IT ON YOUR OWN. SOMETHING YOU HAD TO DO IN ORDER TO HAVE HOPE OF REDEMPTION.
BUT YOUR STRUGGLE IS FAR FROM OVER, DANTE. YOUR MOTHER WAS RIGHT. ERE YOUR JOURNEY ENDS...
...YOUR OWN SINS WILL RETURN TO BEDEVIL YOU.
CRUSADERS--?
THIS CANNOT BE. OUR CAUSE WAS HOLY. WE WERE ABSOLVED!
NO. WE WERE DAMNED.

FRANCESCO...
I WAS DAMNED.
BY YOU.

DANTE! STOP THIS MADNESS!
‹THE CHRISTIANS INTEND TO SLAUGHTER US! WE MUST KILL THEM FIRST!›
‹OVERWHELM THEM WITH NUMBERS!
IT'S OUR ONLY HOPE!›
NO--PLEASE, I'M TRYING TO HELP YOU--
PLEASE DON'T MAKE ME--

NO!
...DAMN YOU...
...DAMN YOU...
...DAMN ME...
YOU CONDEMNED ME HERE.
FRANCESCO... MY BROTHER... YOU MUST KNOW I NEVER MEANT--
OF COURSE NOT. YOU NEVER MEANT TO BETRAY MY SISTER. YOU NEVER MEANT TO SEND ME TO HELL.
BUT YOU DID!
SKANG

FRANCESCO, PLEASE... WERE IT MY CHOICE, I WOULD GLADLY LET YOU KILL ME FOR WHAT I'VE DONE. BUT IT'S YOUR SISTER'S SOUL I SEEK TO SAVE.
THE SOUL YOU CONSIGNED TO LUCIFER WITH YOUR FAITHLESSNESS? HA!
YOU DON'T FOOL ME. YOU WANT BEATRICE FOR YOURSELF.
YOU DON'T DESERVE TO BE MY SISTER'S SLAVE, LET ALONE HER LORD. YOU WISH TO PAY FOR WHAT YOU'VE DONE?
THAT IS A WISH I'LL GLADLY GRANT.
OH, FRANCESCO...
...MY BROTHER...
...FORGIVE ME.

OUR DEEDS WERE DONE...IN THE NAME OF GOD. WHY... HAS HE FORSAKEN US?
IN THE NAME OF GOD? NO.
MURDER IS ONLY IN THE NAME OF THE MURDERER.

NONE DESERVES ABSOLUTION MORE THAN YOU. MAY YOU KNOW THE PEACE IN DEATH I DENIED YOU IN LIFE.
USE MY SOUL WISELY, BROTHER. REDEEM YOURSELF...

FRANCESCO HAS GONE TO HIS REST. YOU HAVE NOT YET EARNED THAT RIGHT.
WALK ON, DANTE. THERE IS A GREAT DISTANCE YET TO TRAVEL.

I KNOW YOU NOT, MONSTER. BUT AFTER WHAT I HAVE JUST DONE, IT WILL BE MY PLEASURE TO FIGHT YOU.
I AM GERYON. AND WE HAVE NO CAUSE TO FIGHT, O MAN. YOU ARE ONE OF US.
BELOW LIES THE EIGHTH CIRCLE. THE DOMAIN OF FRAUD.
COME, I SHALL TAKE YOU THERE.
I CAN THINK OF NO BETTER PLACE FOR A MAN WHO POSED AS ONE DOING GOD'S WORK, ONLY TO COMMIT THE MOST GRIEVOUS SINS.
AND IN SO DOING, DAMNED NOT JUST HIMSELF, BUT THOSE HE LOVES.
IGNORE GERYON'S BARBED WORDS. HE BEARS A GRUDGE AGAINST QUESTING WARRIORS.
HE WAS SLAIN BY HERCULES, IN ONE OF HIS LABORS.
AND HERCULES MET THE END HE DESERVED, DONE IN BY HIS OWN FAITHLESSNESS. I DELIVER YOU ON YOUR WAY IN THE HOPE YOU WILL DO THE SAME.
YOUR MOCKERY CAN ADD NOTHING TO THE PAIN I ALREADY FEEL. SO INSTEAD, MAKE YOURSELF USEFUL...OR YOU, VIRGIL, IF YOUR PRECIOUS RULES ALLOW.
KNOW YOU THE NATURE OF THESE CHAINS I MUST CONSTANTLY SUNDER TO PROCEED?
THOSE WHO SERVE THE INFERNO KNOW ONLY WHAT THEY ARE PERMITTED. THE ANSWER TO YOUR QUESTION IS BEYOND SUCH AS WE.

BUT I KNOW THIS. YOU HAVE FAR MORE PRESSING CONCERNS.
PREPARE TO REAP THE FRUITS OF YOUR MANY SINS.
I CAN GO NO FURTHER, DANTE. WHAT WAITS AHEAD... YOU MUST FACE ALONE. MAY GOD BE WITH YOU.
BEATRICE? IS THAT YOU?
MY LOVE, I'VE COME FOR YOU, AS I PROMISED.
YES, I KNOW YOUR PROMISES WELL.
YOUR PROMISE TO BE TRUE TO ME. YOUR PROMISE TO SERVE GOD, ONLY TO MASSACRE INNOCENTS, AS LUCIFER HAS DELIGHTED IN SHOWING ME.
YOUR PROMISE TO PROTECT MY BROTHER, WHILE INSTEAD YOU DAMN HIM TO THIS PLACE...AND FORCE ME TO WATCH AS YOU CAUSE HIS ***SECOND*** DEATH!
YOU SAW...? BEATRICE, I HAD NO CHOICE! I DID IT FOR ***YOU!***

YOU WANT TO DO SOMETHING FOR ME, DANTE?
DIE.

BEATRICE
DIEGO LATORRE CHARACTER STUDIES

CHAPTER FIVE
DEVASTATION

THERE IS A PLACE IN HELL CALLED THE MALEBOLGE.
WELCOME, DANTE, TO THE EIGHTH CIRCLE--THE DOMAIN OF FRAUD. YOUR ETERNAL HOME.
FOR YOU ARE THE GREATEST FRAUD OF ALL.
BEATRICE, I BEG OF YOU... DO NOT GIVE IN TO WHAT LUCIFER HAS MADE YOU.
DO NOT CORRUPT THE INNOCENT SOUL YOU WERE. THE WOMAN TO WHOM I GAVE MYSELF... TO WHOM I GAVE MY LOVE.
AS IF YOU CARED ONE WHIT ABOUT ME. IF YOU HAD, YOU WOULD NEVER HAVE BETRAYED ME IN THE MOST BASE, THE MOST PAINFUL WAYS IMAGINABLE.
IN THE REALM OF FRAUD, DANTE, YOU ARE KING. PRETENDING TO BE A CHRISTIAN. PRETENDING TO BE A HERO.
PRETENDING TO LOVE ANYONE BUT YOURSELF.
I DO LOVE YOU, BEATRICE.

LIAR!
THERE ARE TEN BOLGI IN THIS PLACE. TEN RINGS, EACH WITH ITS OWN BRAND OF THE SIN OF FRAUD, INHABITED BY ITS OWN DAMNED SOULS. ALL OF WHOM ANSWER TO ME.
HERE, THOSE WHO HAVE BROKEN THE BOND OF TRUST AND LOVE ARE FOREVER PUNISHED. AND NOW, FOR ALL ETERNITY, THEY WILL PUNISH YOU.
MALACODA! SHOW OUR GUEST THE AGONY THAT AWAITS HIM, FROM NOW UNTIL THE END OF TIME!

LOOK AT HIM, MAJESTY. IS HE NOT WORTHY OF YOUR HATE? YOU COULD DESTROY HIM NOW, WITH YOUR OWN HANDS. RIP HIS SOUL TO SHREDS.
SURELY, WITH ALL HE'S DONE TO YOU, HE DESERVES NO LESS.
PANDERER. SEDUCER. I SEE THROUGH YOU, DEMON.
DANTE IS *SLAUGHTERING* YOUR FELLOWS, AND YOU FEAR JOINING THE BATTLE.
I HAD THOUGHT YOUR CIRCLE MIGHT SUIT HIM. BUT IN TRUTH, I REQUIRED NO CONVINCING TO LIE WITH HIM. NOR DID THE SLUT HE DISHONORED ME WITH.
YOUR ILK CANNOT HOPE TO DEFEAT HIM.
MERCEEE--

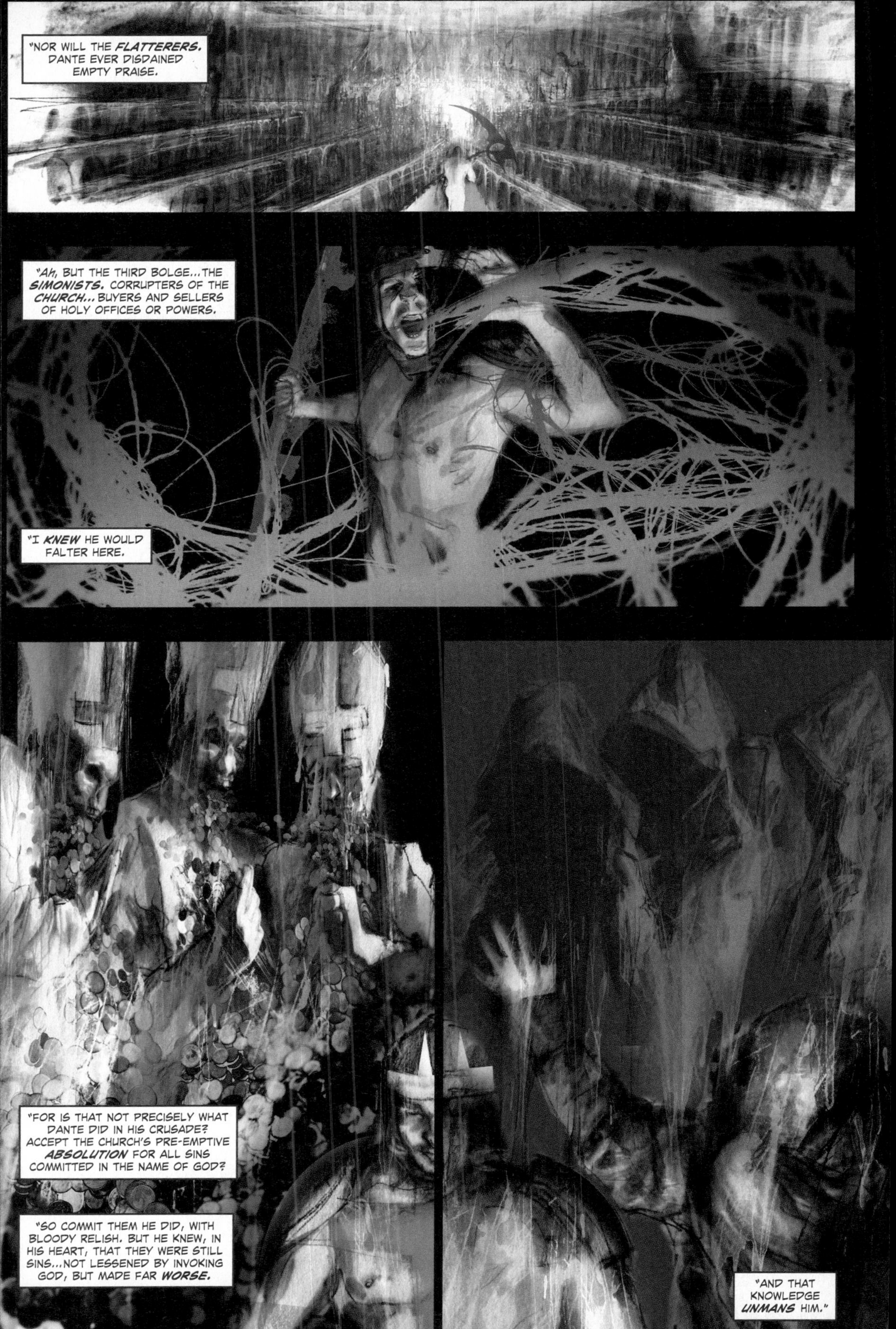
"NOR WILL THE *FLATTERERS.* DANTE EVER DISDAINED EMPTY PRAISE.
"*Ah*, BUT THE THIRD BOLGE... THE *SIMONISTS.* CORRUPTERS OF THE *CHURCH...* BUYERS AND SELLERS OF HOLY OFFICES OR POWERS.
"I *KNEW* HE WOULD FALTER HERE.
"FOR IS THAT NOT PRECISELY WHAT DANTE DID IN HIS CRUSADE? ACCEPT THE CHURCH'S PRE-EMPTIVE *ABSOLUTION* FOR ALL SINS COMMITTED IN THE NAME OF GOD?
"SO COMMIT THEM HE DID, WITH BLOODY RELISH. BUT HE KNEW, IN HIS HEART, THAT THEY WERE STILL SINS... NOT LESSENED BY INVOKING GOD, BUT MADE FAR *WORSE.*
"AND THAT KNOWLEDGE *UNMANS* HIM."

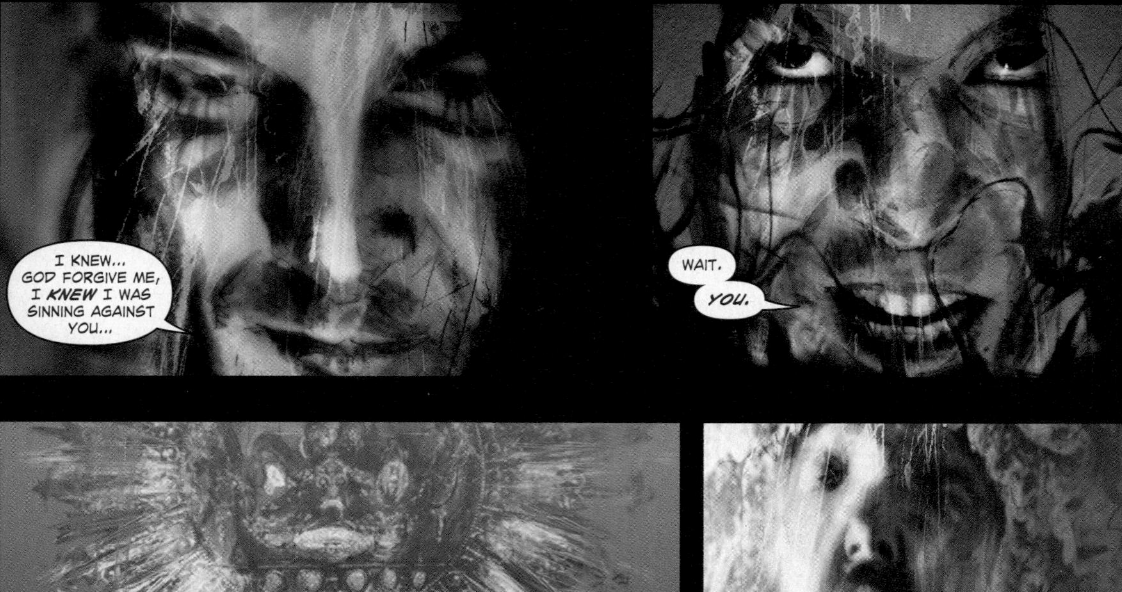
I KNEW... GOD FORGIVE ME, I KNEW I WAS SINNING AGAINST YOU...
WAIT. YOU.

FALSE BISHOP! YOU SWORE TO ME AND MY FELLOWS THAT WE FOUGHT IN A HOLY CAUSE!
THAT THOUGH WE COMMIT THE MOST MORTAL OF SINS, WE WOULD BE HELD BLAMELESS!

I... I BELIEVED IT, DANTE! I TOO WAS DECEIVED!

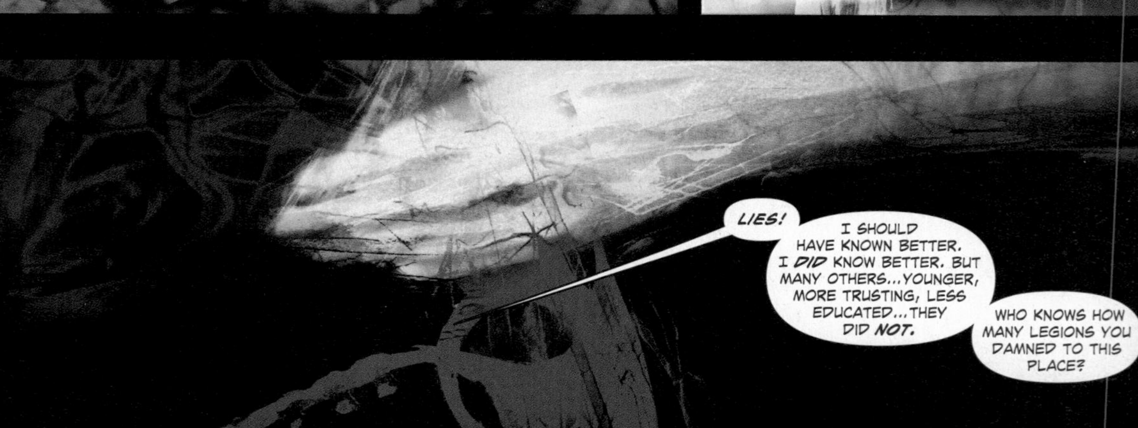
LIES!
I SHOULD HAVE KNOWN BETTER. I DID KNOW BETTER. BUT MANY OTHERS...YOUNGER, MORE TRUSTING, LESS EDUCATED...THEY DID NOT.
WHO KNOWS HOW MANY LEGIONS YOU DAMNED TO THIS PLACE?

IN THEIR NAME I STRIKE!
IN THEIR NAME I FIGHT ON!
NOT FOR MYSELF, BUT FOR THOSE WHO DESERVE *BETTER!*
I MUST CONFESS...HE IS IMPRESSIVE.

"THE SIGHT OF THE SORCERERS OF THE FOURTH BOLGE STRIKES FEAR INTO THE BRAVEST.
"YET HE FIGHTS ON.
"STILL, INEVITABLY, THE UNENDING BATTLE WEARS UPON HIM. THE DEMONIC MALEBRANCHE OF THE FIFTH BOLGE PAUSE IN THEIR TORMENT OF POLITICIANS TO HURL THEIR BARBS AT HIM...
"...AND THE ATTACK BEGINS TO TELL. INFLICTING PAIN UNIMAGINABLE TO MOST.

"BUT LOOK. WHERE MOST WOULD FALL, DANTE SEEMS TO DRAW STRENGTH FROM HIS ORDEAL.

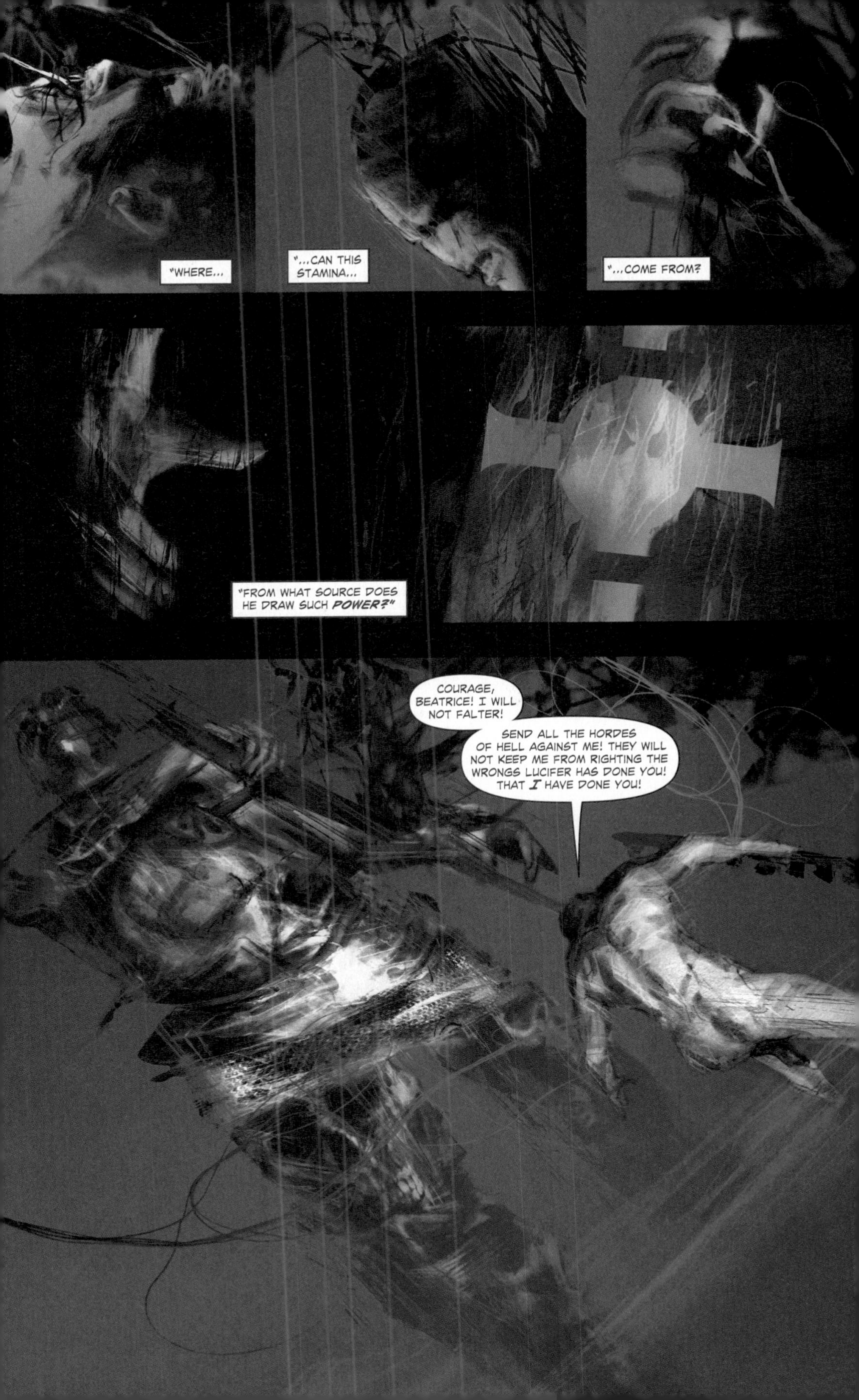
"WHERE...
"...CAN THIS STAMINA...
"...COME FROM?
"FROM WHAT SOURCE DOES HE DRAW SUCH POWER?"
COURAGE, BEATRICE! I WILL NOT FALTER!
SEND ALL THE HORDES OF HELL AGAINST ME! THEY WILL NOT KEEP ME FROM RIGHTING THE WRONGS LUCIFER HAS DONE YOU! THAT I HAVE DONE YOU!

COULD IT BE... HE SPEAKS THE *TRUTH?*
"I CONSIDERED HIS SINS THE WORST FORM OF HYPOCRISY. YET HE HAS VANQUISHED THE HYPOCRITES OF THE SIXTH BOLGE AND PROCEEDS INTO THE SEVENTH...

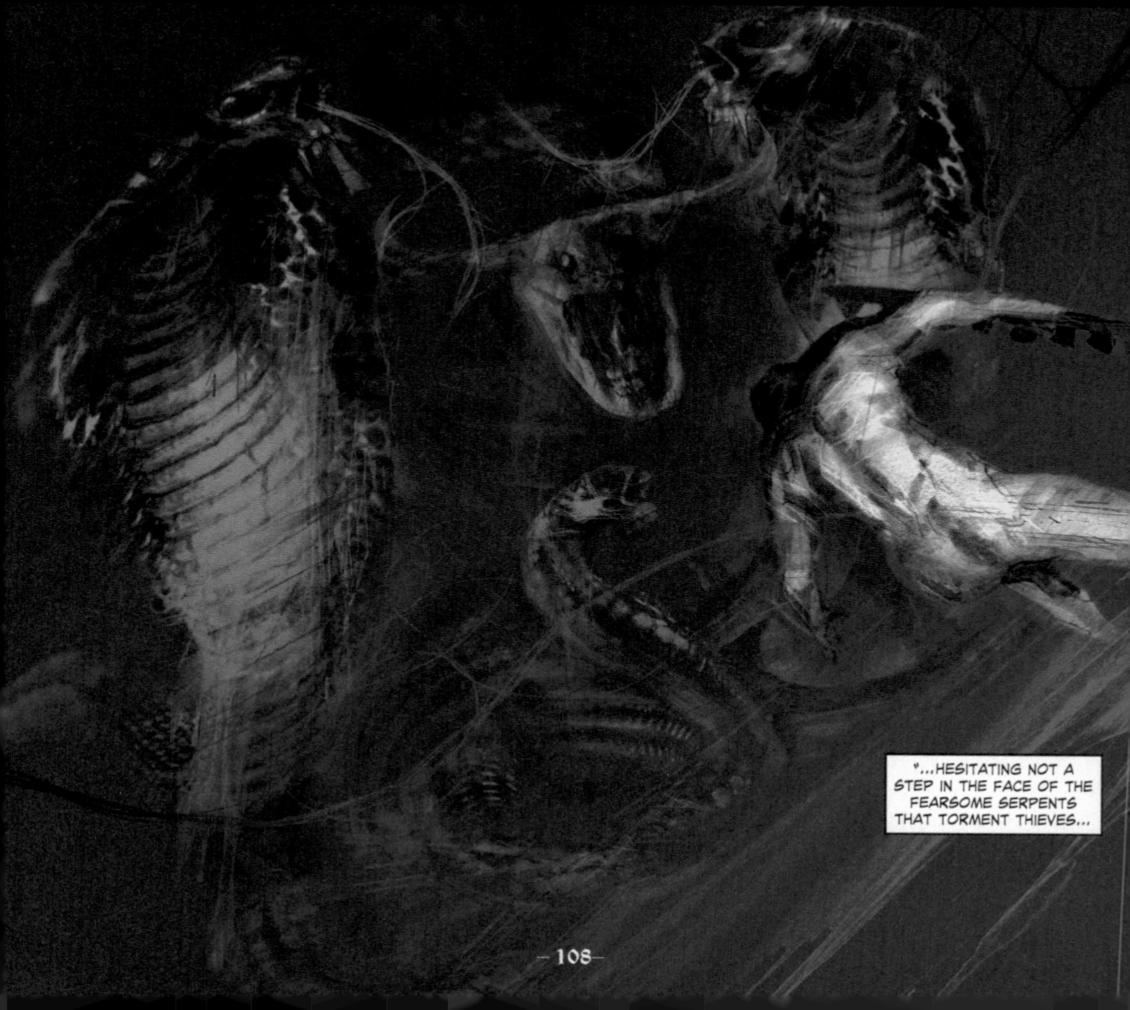
"...HESITATING NOT A STEP IN THE FACE OF THE FEARSOME SERPENTS THAT TORMENT THIEVES...

"...OR THE ETERNAL FLAME THAT CONSUMES THE EVIL COUNSELORS IN THE EIGHTH BOLGE."
I COME, BEATRICE!
"HE RENDS THE FABRIC OF HELL ITSELF TO REACH ME...
"...COLLAPSING THE VERY WALLS OF THIS CIRCLE UPON HIS ENEMIES, SNUFFING THEIR FLAMES.
"CAN THE BRAVE, GENTLE SOUL I FELL IN LOVE WITH AND THE SINNER I HAVE SEEN REVEALED BE ONE AND THE SAME MAN?
"DOES HE TRULY REPENT OF HIS ACTIONS?

"IF SO, I DESPAIR AT THE THOUGHT OF WHAT HE MUST OVERCOME TO SAVE HIS SOUL...AND MINE...FROM THIS INFERNAL PLACE.
"THE SOWERS OF DISCORD IN THE NINTH BOLGE ARE FEARSOME...
"...BUT DANTE CUTS THEM INTO STILL SMALLER PIECES.
"AND THE TENTH BOLGE--THE FALSIFIERS--I THOUGHT IT IMPOSSIBLE FOR ANYONE TO ESCAPE THE VIRULENT, LEPROUS DISEASES THAT THEY VOMIT FORTH.
"YET HE SEEMS UNAFFECTED. PROTECTED BY A LIGHT THAT APPEARS TO COME FROM WITHIN.
"CAN IT BE HIS FAITH IS SO STRONG? IS THERE HOPE?
"MY HEART BEGINS TO SOFTEN...
"...BUT TO OVERCOME HIS FINAL TRIAL, DANTE WILL NEED MY HELP. I MUST--"

ah, THERE'S my lovely bride. still playing with your wedding present, I see.
after all, now that we are man and wife, there should be no SECRETS between us...don't you agree?
BEGONE, LUCIFER. YOU GAVE THIS MAN TO ME, NOW LET ME DEAL WITH HIM.
oh, I intend to. but first I felt it would sweeten the pot a bit--and banish any...LINGERING DOUBTS you might feel--to show you a final revelation.
LUCIFER! I HAVE DEFEATED ALL THE HORDES OF HELL YOU SENT AGAINST ME! YOUR DEMON ARMY, THE MALACODA, COULD NOT KEEP ME FROM MY LOVE!
idiot. the dwellers of the malebolge are NOT malacoda.
malacoda is their COMMANDER.
face him now, and annoy me no more.

now then. where were we?
ARGH!
ENOUGH GAMES. I DO NOT FEAR YOU, LUCIFER. I DEFY YOU. I NO LONGER WISH TO PUNISH DANTE.
ah, but wait. make no declarations until you sample the last tidbit in the feast of pain dante has served you...

GOD IN HEAVEN...ALL THE PRISONERS... MURDERED...
WHO IS RESPONSIBLE FOR THIS SLAUGHTER?
ANSWER ME! RICHARD THE LIONHEART COMMANDS IT!

TAKE CARE OF MY SISTER.
WHAT? FRANCESCO, WHAT DO YOU--

MY KING...I AM RESPONSIBLE.
HANG HIM.

PREPARE TO MARCH TONIGHT! WHEN NOBLE SALADIN LEARNS OF THIS ATROCITY, HE WILL BRING FORTH THE FIRES OF HELL!
KING RICHARD, WAIT.

YOU HAVE SOMETHING TO SAY, SOLDIER?

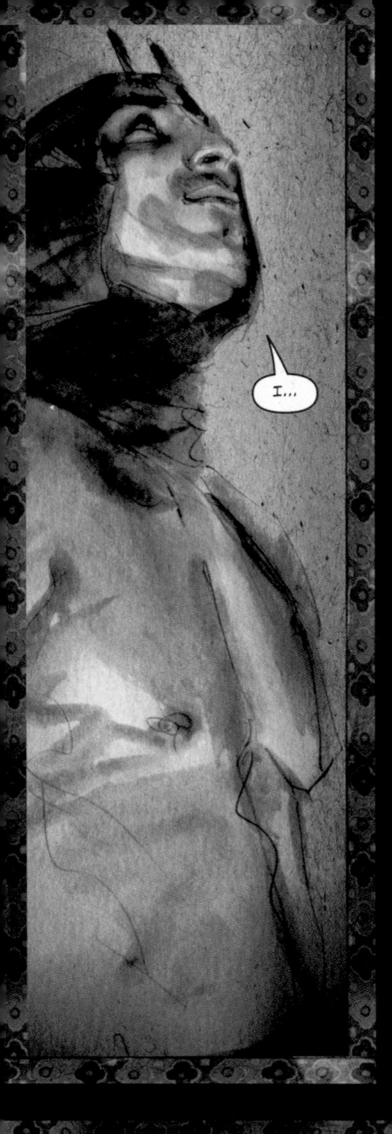
I...

...NO.

GOD FORGIVE ME.

...NO...
...MY POOR BROTHER...
SUCH A TRAGEDY. FIRST DAMNED BY DANTE, THEN KILLED FOR HIS CRIMES.
DOES IT NOT MAKE YOU WANT TO REND HIM INTO BLOODY BITS?
IT MAKES ME WANT TO DIE.
BUT HERE, EVEN THAT MERCY IS DENIED ME.
TAKE ME, LUCIFER. WE ARE HUSBAND AND WIFE. LET OUR UNION BE MORE THAN SYMBOLIC.
LAY WITH ME. LET ME BETRAY DANTE AS HE BETRAYED ME. KNOW ME IN HIS SIGHT, WITH HIM HELPLESS TO PREVENT IT.
I--

HELL IS FULL OF WHORES. I HAVE NO DESIRE FOR YOU WHEN YOU BEHAVE LIKE ONE.
IF YOU WISH DANTE TO SUFFER, ATTEND TO IT YOURSELF.
PERHAPS THEN YOU'LL BE WORTHY OF MY ATTENTIONS.
MY GOD... I UNDERSTAND.
YOU MAY DECEIVE, MANIPULATE, CAJOLE. YOU MAY LIE AND BARGAIN AND TRICK.
BUT YOU ARE AS MUCH A PRISONER AS ANY SOUL HERE.
IN ALL THE WAYS THAT MATTER... THE DEVIL IS IMPOTENT.
BUT I AM NOT.

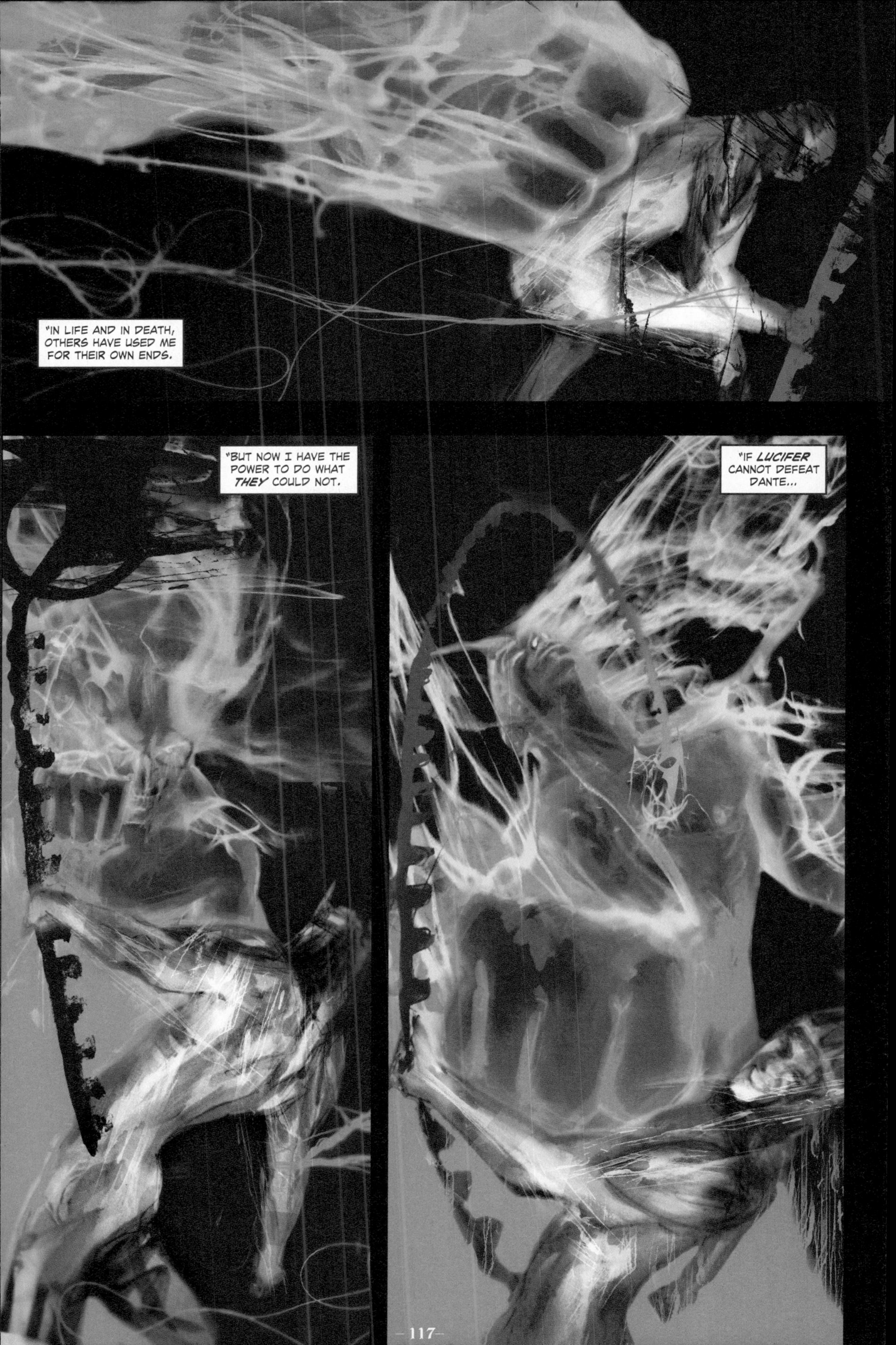
"IN LIFE AND IN DEATH, OTHERS HAVE USED ME FOR THEIR OWN ENDS.
"BUT NOW I HAVE THE POWER TO DO WHAT *THEY* COULD NOT.
"IF *LUCIFER* CANNOT DEFEAT DANTE...

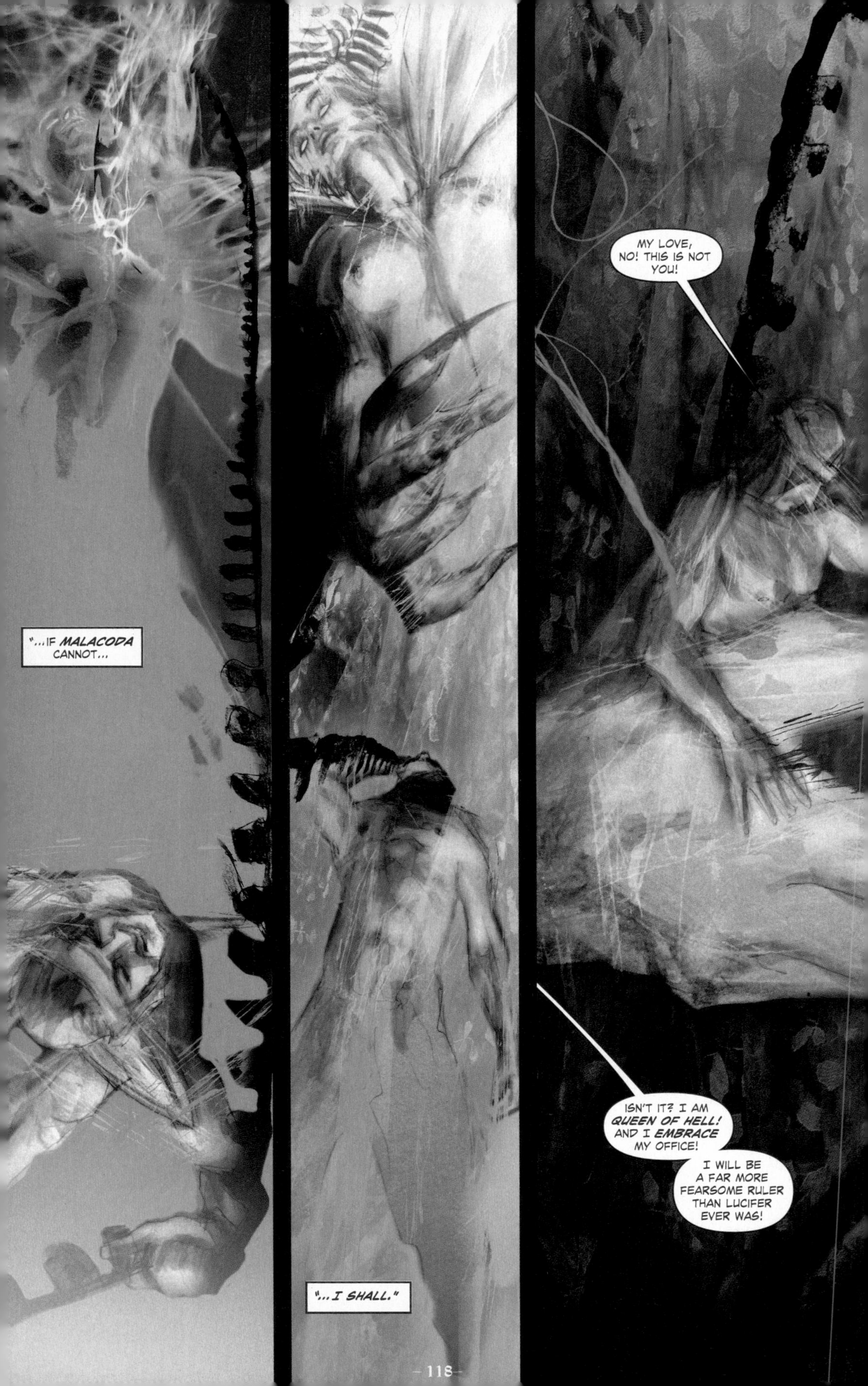
"...IF MALACODA CANNOT...
"...I SHALL."
MY LOVE, NO! THIS IS NOT YOU!
ISN'T IT? I AM QUEEN OF HELL! AND I EMBRACE MY OFFICE!
I WILL BE A FAR MORE FEARSOME RULER THAN LUCIFER EVER WAS!

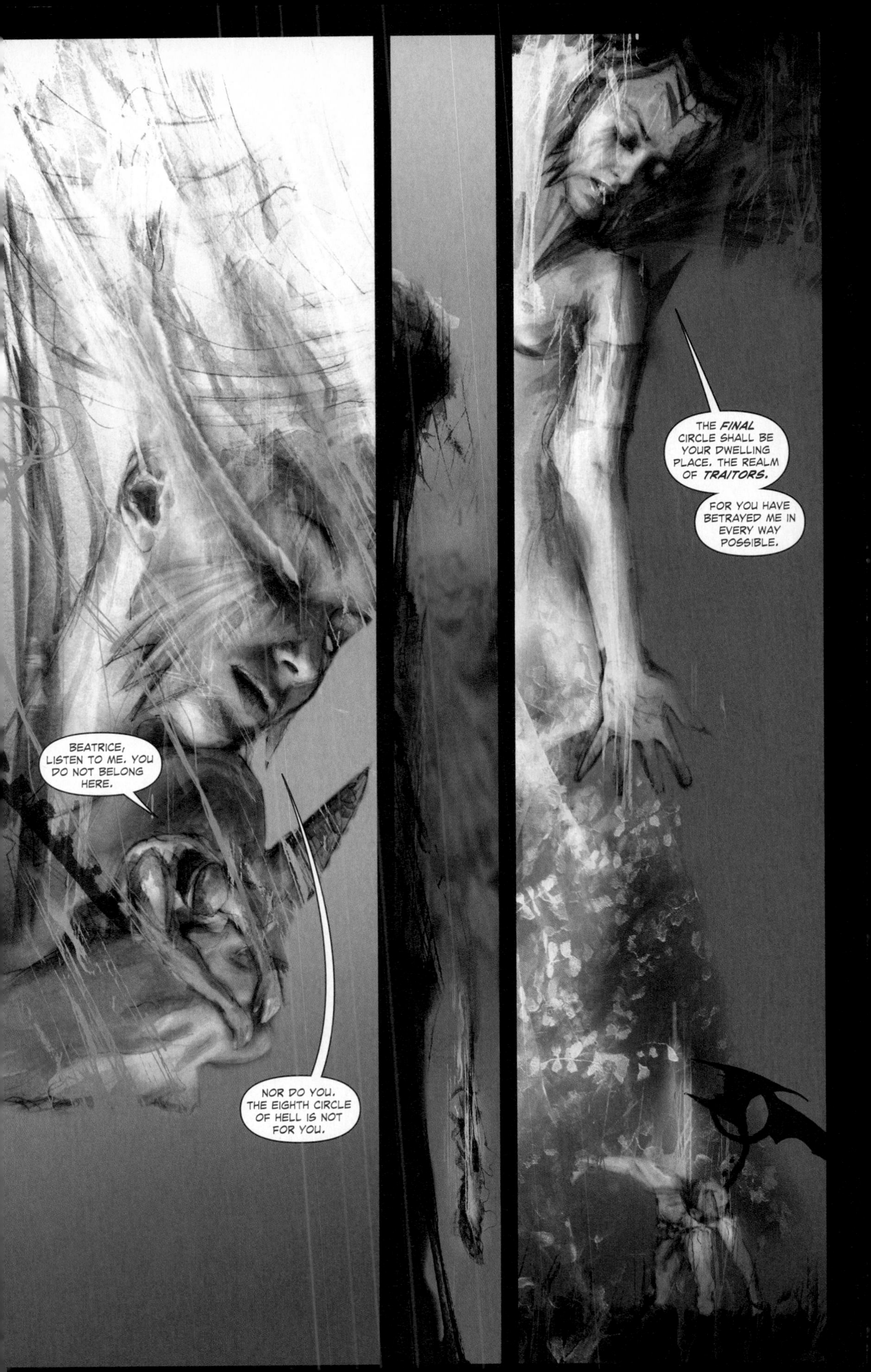

BEATRICE, LISTEN TO ME. YOU DO NOT BELONG HERE.
NOR DO YOU. THE EIGHTH CIRCLE OF HELL IS NOT FOR YOU.
THE *FINAL* CIRCLE SHALL BE YOUR DWELLING PLACE. THE REALM OF ***TRAITORS.***
FOR YOU HAVE BETRAYED ME IN EVERY WAY POSSIBLE.

AND NOW, AT LONG LAST...
...YOU WILL PAY!

COVER CONCEPTS FOR ISSUES 1-6
BY DIEGO LATORRE

CHAPTER SIX
defeat

YOU BETRAYED ME. SLAUGHTERED INNOCENTS. ALLOWED MY BROTHER, WHOM YOU SWORE TO PROTECT, TO HANG FOR YOUR CRIMES.
YOU DAMNED MY IMMORTAL SOUL-- THE SOUL OF THE WOMAN YOU CLAIMED TO LOVE--TO HELL FOR ALL ETERNITY.
NOW, DANTE... BEFORE I WREAK MY TERRIBLE VENGEANCE UPON YOU...BEFORE I ANNIHILATE YOUR VERY SPIRIT... I DEMAND AN ACCOUNTING!
LET ME HEAR THE FEEBLE EXCUSES YOU MOUTHED AS ONE TREACHERY AFTER ANOTHER WAS EXPOSED. ANSWER FOR YOUR SINS. JUSTIFY THEM, IF YOU HAVE THE AUDACITY!

...I...
...I CANNOT.

I GIVE UP ON THIS JOURNEY.
YOU ARE CORRECT. I AM A SINNER, AND MY PLACE IS IN HELL.
BUT YOURS IS IN PARADISE. IF MY ACTIONS HAVE DENIED YOU YOUR RIGHTFUL REWARD, I DESERVE WHATEVER PUNISHMENT I RECEIVE.
I AM TRULY SORRY FOR WHAT I HAVE DONE. MAY YOU ONE DAY FORGIVE ME.

HE... REPENTS?
NO. HE BEGS FOR MERCY, LIKE THE DECEIVER HE IS. TRIES TO TAKE ADVANTAGE OF OUR LOVE ONCE AGAIN. GIVE HIM WHAT HE ASKS. CRUSH HIM!
HE IS A SINNER MANY TIMES OVER! HE DESERVES DAMNATION! HE IS NOT THE MAN YOU LOVE!
ISN'T HE?
CAN THE GENTLE SOUL I FELL IN LOVE WITH AND THE WRATHFUL KILLER, THE LUSTFUL BETRAYER NOT EXIST IN THE SAME MAN?
ARE WE NOT ALL CAPABLE OF BOTH? HAVE I, IN MY JOURNEY THROUGH THE INFERNO, NOT SUCCUMBED TO THE VERY SAME SINS? WRATH, PRIDE, TREACHERY...
DO I NOT STAND READY TO DESTROY THE ONE I PROFESSED TO LOVE?
YOU STAND READY TO METE OUT JUSTICE. PUNISHMENT WELL DESERVED.
I...I...

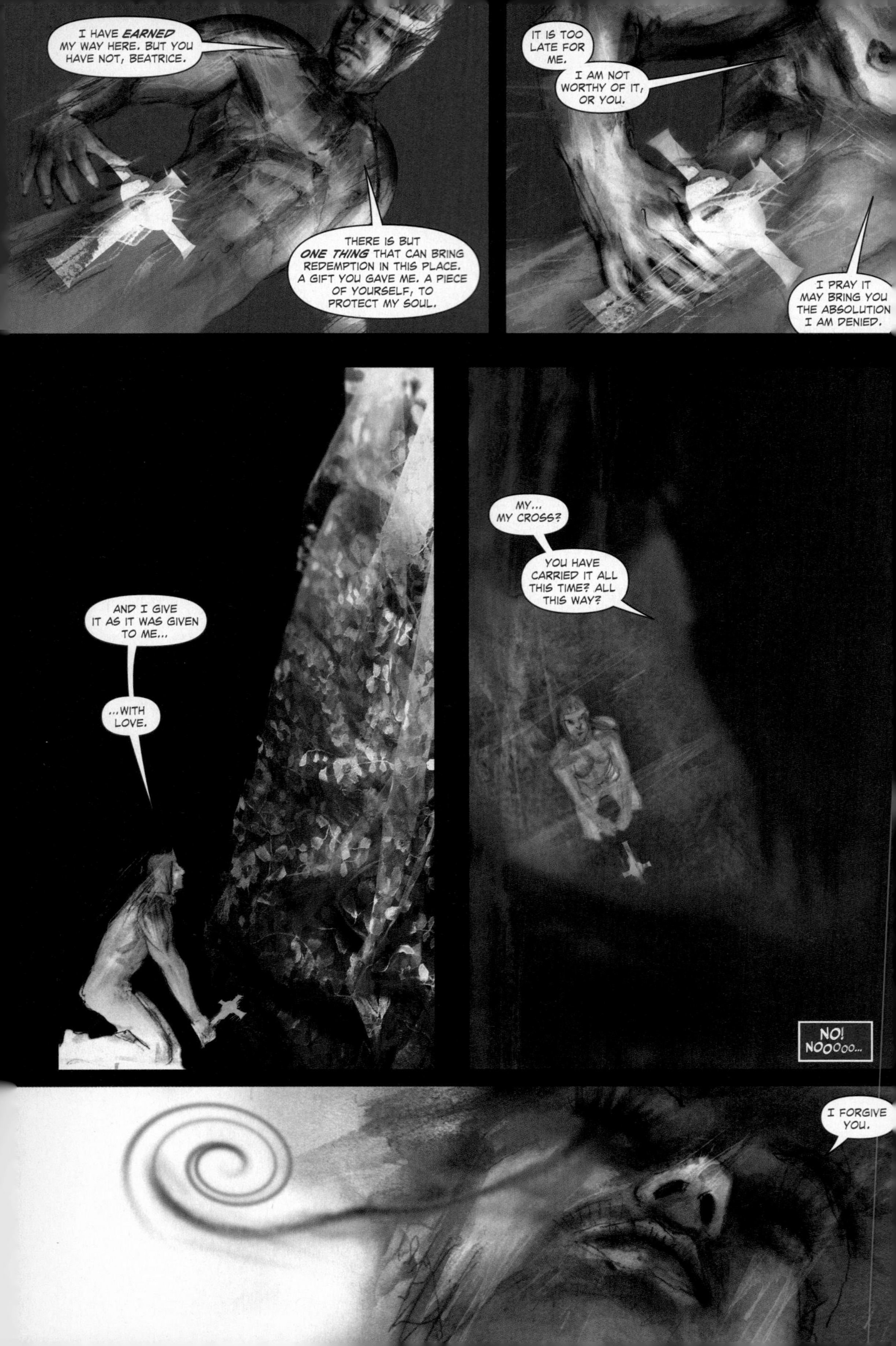
I HAVE EARNED MY WAY HERE. BUT YOU HAVE NOT, BEATRICE.
THERE IS BUT ONE THING THAT CAN BRING REDEMPTION IN THIS PLACE. A GIFT YOU GAVE ME. A PIECE OF YOURSELF, TO PROTECT MY SOUL.
IT IS TOO LATE FOR ME.
I AM NOT WORTHY OF IT, OR YOU.
I PRAY IT MAY BRING YOU THE ABSOLUTION I AM DENIED.
AND I GIVE IT AS IT WAS GIVEN TO ME...
...WITH LOVE.
MY... MY CROSS?
YOU HAVE CARRIED IT ALL THIS TIME? ALL THIS WAY?
NO! NOOooo...
I FORGIVE YOU.

FSAESHH
BEATRICE?

BEATRICE!

BEATRICE...
IT IS I, DANTE.
WE ARE REUNITED, AT LONG LAST.

A REUNION I FEAR WILL BE SHORT-LIVED.
FOR BEATRICE HAS CHOSEN LOVE OVER WRATH...FORGIVENESS OVER REVENGE. SHE DOES NOT BELONG HERE.
WHO--?

A MESSENGER. FROM A BETTER PLACE.
I... UNDERSTAND.
I DO **NOT.** PROVE TO ME YOU ARE NOT SOME NEW TRICK OF LUCIFER'S, OR--
YOU'VE DONE WELL, DANTE. THOUGH YOU MAY NOT REALIZE IT NOW, YOU HAVE SAVED MUCH MORE THAN THIS INNOCENT SOUL.
HE SPEAKS TRULY, MY LOVE. YOUR ROLE IN THE ONGOING BATTLE IS MORE SIGNIFICANT THAN YOU CAN IMAGINE... MORE IMPORTANT, EVEN, THAN OUR LOVE.
BUT TAKE HEART. I KNOW YOU CAN DO WHAT IS NECESSARY. AND I KNOW YOUR REDEMPTION IS NEAR.
WAIT. I HAVE COME THIS FAR...MUST WE BE PARTED SO SOON?

HAVE FAITH.
YOU WILL SEE ME AGAIN...

DANTE. MY CONGRATULATIONS. BEATRICE'S PRESENCE IN HELL WAS THE GRAVEST INJUSTICE.
VIRGIL. I DIDN'T THINK I'D SEE YOU AGAIN, POET.
I SWORE TO GUIDE YOU ON YOUR JOURNEY.
AND ONE MORE CIRCLE OF THE INFERNO REMAINS.
"INFERNO." YOU HAVE A CURIOUS DEFINITION OF THE WORD.
YOU WALK UPON THE FROZEN WASTES OF ***LAKE COCYTUS.*** THE FARTHEST POINT FROM PARADISE.
THE ***NINTH CIRCLE OF HELL.***

HERE RESIDE THE ***TRAITORS,*** MOST DESPISED OF ALL SINNERS. THEY HAVE NO LOVE, SO THEY ARE DENIED LOVE FOREVER.
THIS IS ***ANTENORA,*** THE FIRST OF FOUR RINGS. WHERE TRAITORS TO COUNTRY ARE PUNISHED.
AND IN ***PTOLOMEA,*** TRAITORS TO GUESTS AND HOSTS MEET THEIR FATE.

HERE IN ***CAINA...***
...TRAITORS TO THEIR OWN KIND FIND JUSTICE.
I CANNOT IMAGINE...
WHAT WORST OF ALL SINNERS...
...ARE IMPRISONED IN THE ***FINAL*** CIRCLE.
THERE IS BUT ***ONE*** OCCUPANT OF ***JUDECCA.***
BUT I FEAR YOU MUST FACE HIM ALONE.
HIM...

...AND HIS GUARDIANS. THE GIANTS NIMROD, EPHIALTES AND ANTAEUS.
FAREWELL, DANTE. I MUST LEAVE YOU NOW, ARMED ONLY WITH WHAT YOUR QUEST HAS BESTOWED UPON YOU. MY JOURNEY ENDS HERE.
I PRAY THE SAME IS NOT TRUE OF YOURS.
TOOM
TOOM
TOOM

COME THIS FAR, ONLY TO FALL?
NEVER.
I HAVE FALLEN AS FAR AS I INTEND TO.
BUT MY ENEMIES...

...LET THEIR FALL SHAKE HELL ITSELF!

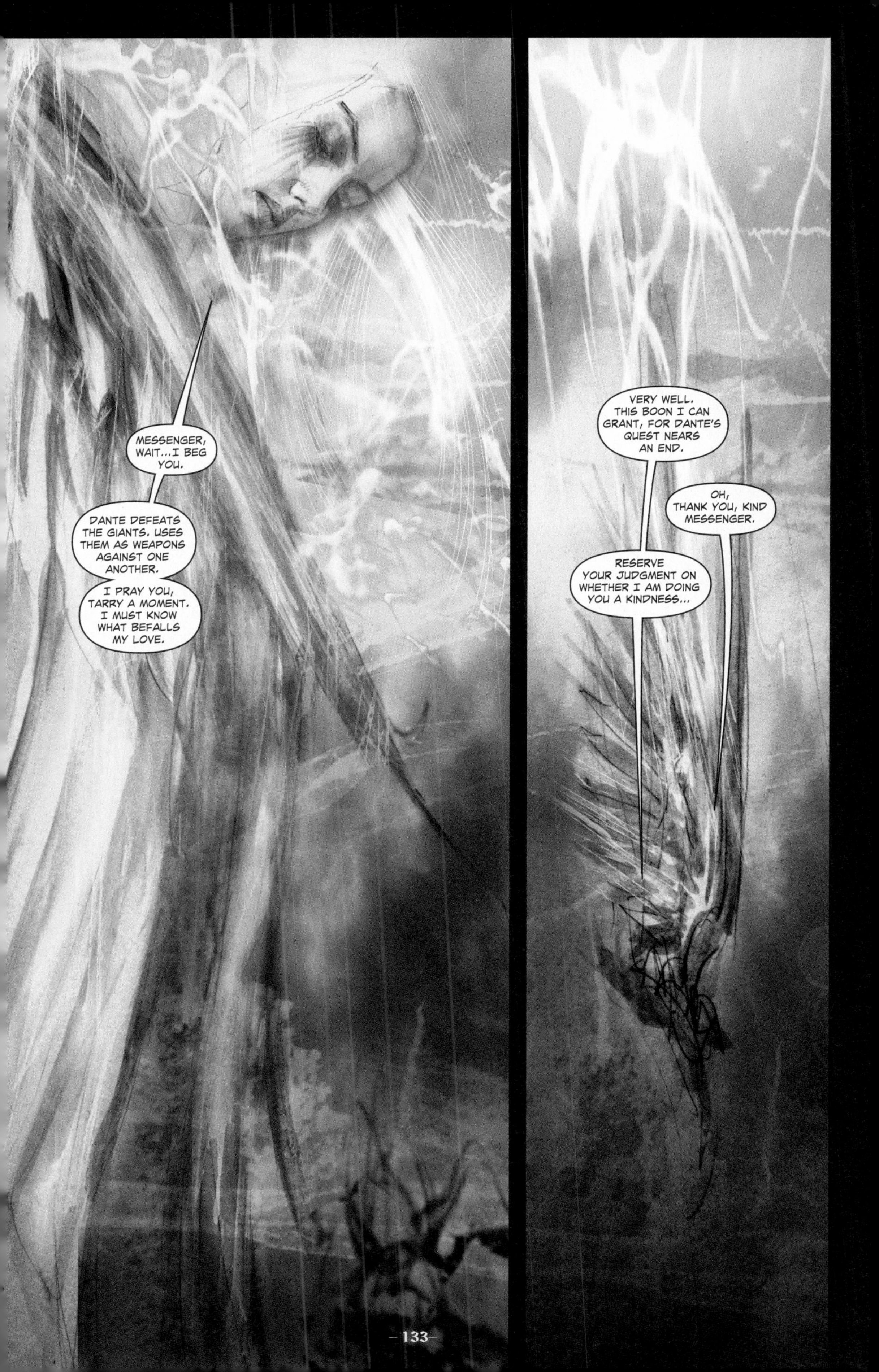
MESSENGER, WAIT...I BEG YOU.
DANTE DEFEATS THE GIANTS. USES THEM AS WEAPONS AGAINST ONE ANOTHER.
I PRAY YOU, TARRY A MOMENT. I MUST KNOW WHAT BEFALLS MY LOVE.
VERY WELL. THIS BOON I CAN GRANT, FOR DANTE'S QUEST NEARS AN END.
OH, THANK YOU, KIND MESSENGER.
RESERVE YOUR JUDGMENT ON WHETHER I AM DOING YOU A KINDNESS...

"...UNTIL THE FINAL OUTCOME HAS REVEALED ITSELF."
AGAIN? AT THE VERY CENTER OF HELL, I FIND ONLY ANOTHER OF THESE INFERNAL CHAINS?
MY PATIENCE IS AT AN END!
DO NOT MOCK ME, LUCIFER!

FACE ME!!
"YOU KNOW NOT WHAT YOU ASK, MY LOVE.

"BUT YOU SHALL RECEIVE IT NONETHELESS.
"GOD HAVE MERCY ON YOU."

AH, AT LAST WE FACE EACH OTHER AS MEN.
CONGRATULATIONS, DANTE. MANY HAVE TRIED, AND MANY HAVE FAILED. ULYSSES, ALEXANDER, ATTILA... ONLY *YOU* POSSESSED A SOUL BLACK ENOUGH TO FREE ME FROM MY CHAINS.
I GAVE MY SOUL TO FREE *BEATRICE,* NOT YOU.
WE HAVE DISCUSSED THE FRUITS OF GOOD INTENTIONS, HAVE WE NOT?

DAMNATION IS YOUR REWARD!
I HAVE SLAIN MANY A GIANT IN MY JOURNEY...

...BUT NONE WITH MORE PLEASURE!

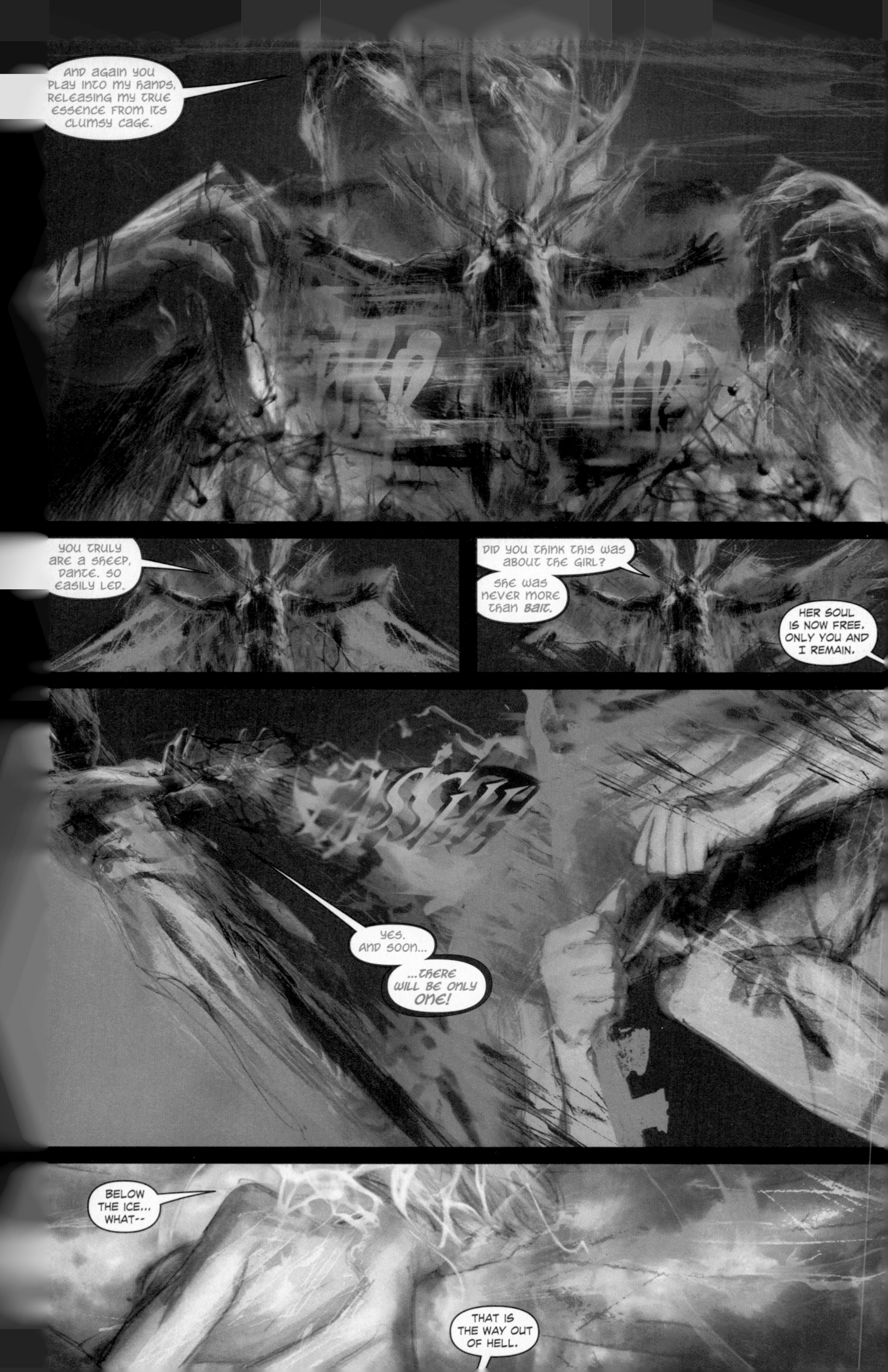
And again you play into my hands, releasing my true essence from its clumsy cage.
You truly are a sheep, Dante. So easily led.
Did you think this was about the girl?
She was never more than bait.
Her soul is now free. Only you and I remain.
Yes. And soon...
...there will be only one!
Below the ice... what--
That is the way out of Hell.

THEN MY SUSPICIONS ARE CORRECT. HE DOES NOT SEEK TO SLAY DANTE AT ALL.
NO. LIKE ALL WHO DWELL WITHIN, LUCIFER DESIRES NOTHING MORE THAN TO ESCAPE HELL. IF DANTE CANNOT DEFEAT HIM, THE EVIL ONE WILL BREAK THROUGH TO THE NEXT REALM.
BUT HELL MUST HAVE A MONARCH.
SO I... I WAS MORE THAN BAIT.
THE PRINCE OF LIES SPOKE ONE TRUTH. HE TRULY SOUGHT TO MAKE ME QUEEN OF HELL... SO THAT I MIGHT TAKE HIS PLACE.
INDEED. AND NOW THAT YOU ARE BEYOND HIS REACH...
...HE MUST FIND ANOTHER.
SHNKK
OH, NO...
...DANTE...

CAN I NOT WARN HIM?
I FEAR NOT, LADY BEATRICE. IF DANTE IS TO PREVENT DISASTER, IF HE IS TO SAVE HIMSELF...
...HE MUST **REDEEM HIMSELF.**
YOU FIND YOUR FINAL DEFEAT AMUSING, MONSTER?
POOR, DELUDED CREATURE.
YOU SEE IT BEFORE YOUR EYES, AND RECOGNIZE IT NOT. THIS IS NO DEFEAT.
YOU ARE PRIVILEGED TO WITNESS LUCIFER'S FINAL...

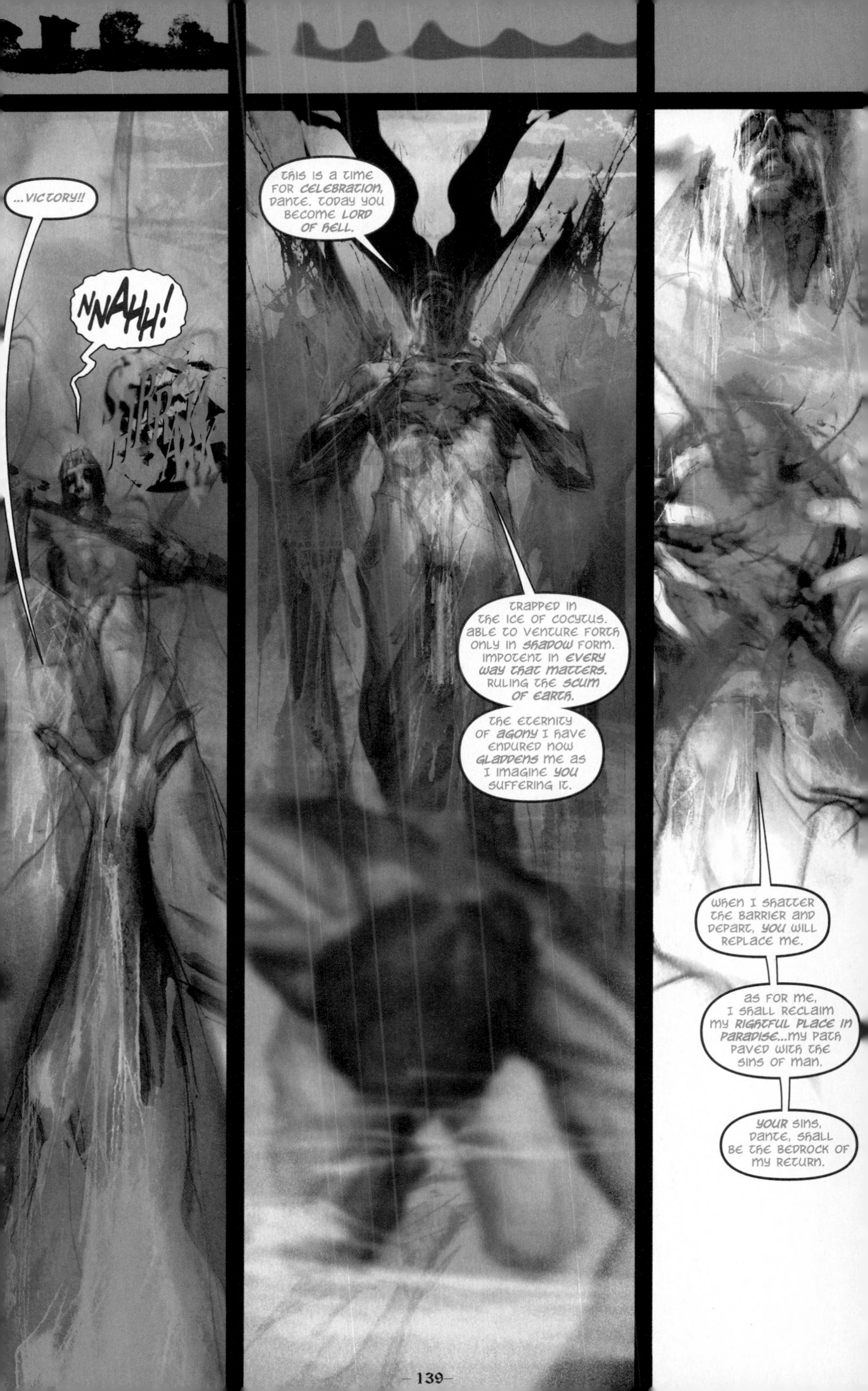
...VICTORY!!
NNAHH!
THIS IS A TIME FOR CELEBRATION, DANTE. TODAY YOU BECOME LORD OF HELL.
TRAPPED IN THE ICE OF COCYTUS. ABLE TO VENTURE FORTH ONLY IN SHADOW FORM. IMPOTENT IN EVERY WAY THAT MATTERS. RULING THE SCUM OF EARTH.
THE ETERNITY OF AGONY I HAVE ENDURED NOW GLADDENS ME AS I IMAGINE YOU SUFFERING IT.
WHEN I SHATTER THE BARRIER AND DEPART, YOU WILL REPLACE ME.
AS FOR ME, I SHALL RECLAIM MY RIGHTFUL PLACE IN PARADISE...MY PATH PAVED WITH THE SINS OF MAN.
YOUR SINS, DANTE, SHALL BE THE BEDROCK OF MY RETURN.

AND ALL THAT IS GOOD SHALL BE GONE FROM THE UNIVERSE FOREVER!
NOT...
...YET.
YOU ARE RIGHT. ALONE, I HAVE NO HOPE OF DEFEATING YOU.
BUT I AM NOT ALONE.
I HAVE MET MANY SOULS SUFFERING IN THIS PLACE. LIKE YOU, THEY WANT NOTHING MORE THAN TO LEAVE.
BUT FIRST...

...THEY WISH TO THANK YOU FOR YOUR HOSPITALITY!
MOTHER! FATHER! BROTHERS!
ABSOLVE ME!
NO! WAIT!
THIS POWER, DANTE...WE COULD USE IT TOGETHER. RULE TOGETHER.
I CAN REUNITE YOU WITH BEATRICE. WE COULD RULE THE THREE KINGDOMS OF THE AFTERLIFE! ALL YOU DESIRE CAN BE YOURS!
ALL I DESIRE...
...IS TO BE DONE WITH YOU.
noooo...

YOU HAVE WON, DANTE. LUCIFER IS TRAPPED, AGAIN AND FOR ALL TIME.
THANK YOU, MOTHER. GODSPEED ON YOUR JOURNEY... MAY ALL OF YOU FIND YOUR REWARD.
IT IS NOT ONLY *WE* WHO HAVE EARNED A REWARD, MY SON.
COME, DANTE. COME OUT OF THIS PLACE.
WHERE--?
DANTE...

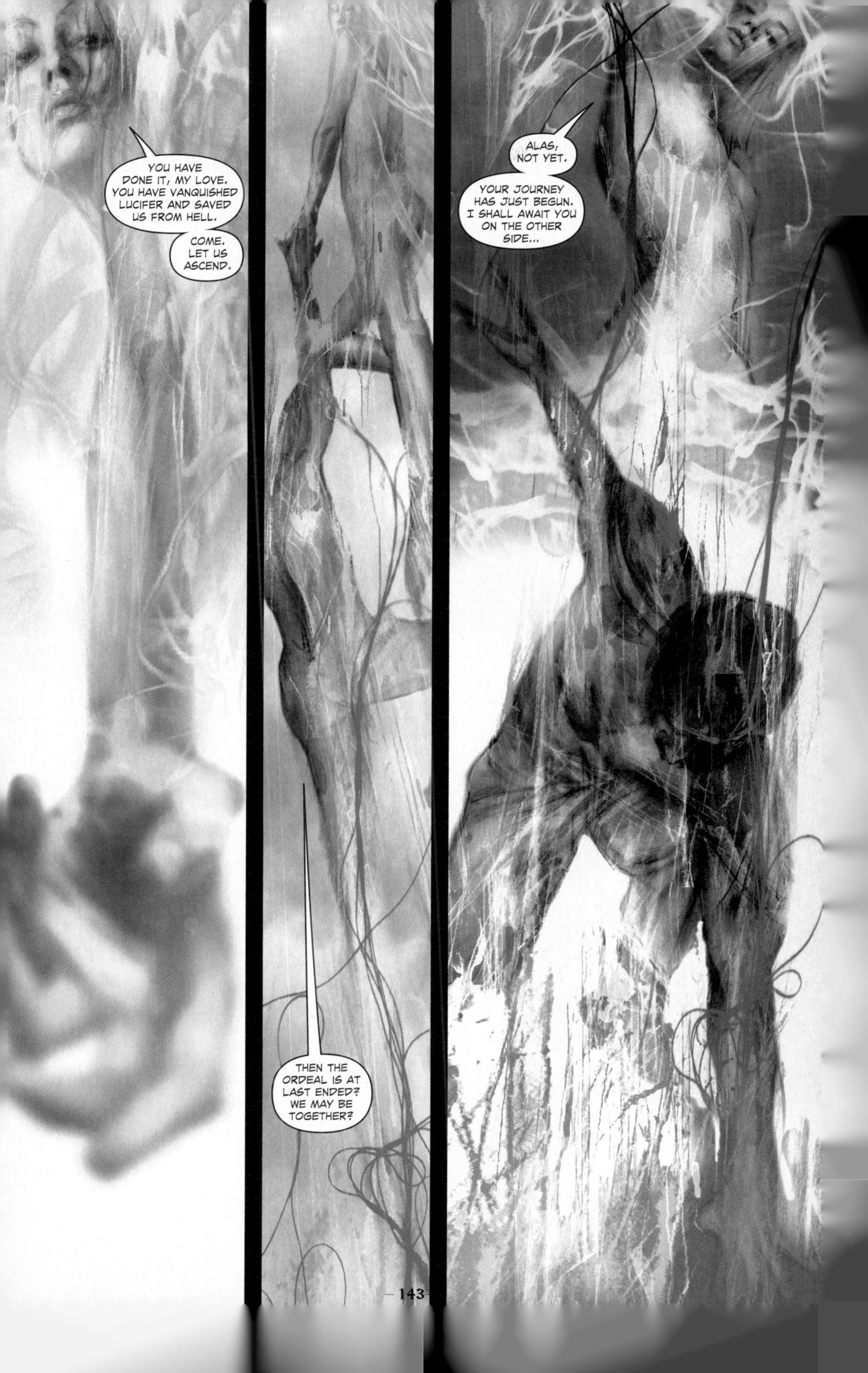
YOU HAVE DONE IT, MY LOVE. YOU HAVE VANQUISHED LUCIFER AND SAVED US FROM HELL.
COME. LET US ASCEND.
THEN THE ORDEAL IS AT LAST ENDED? WE MAY BE TOGETHER?
ALAS, NOT YET.
YOUR JOURNEY HAS JUST BEGUN. I SHALL AWAIT YOU ON THE OTHER SIDE...

...OF
PURGATORY.

The end. . . for now.